Chaim Walder

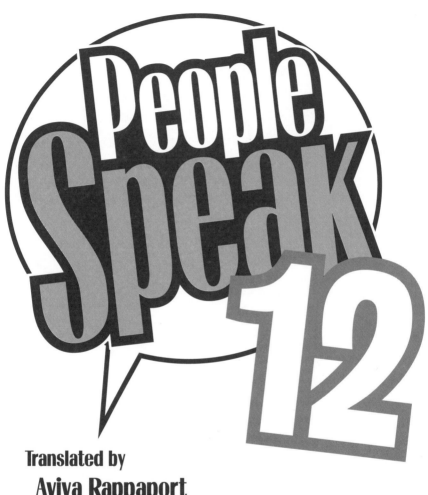

Translated by
Aviva Rappaport

FELDHEIM PUBLISHERS
JERUSALEM NEW YORK

ISBN 978-1-68025-468-6

Translated by Aviva Rappaport
Proofread by Cindy Scarr

DISTRIBUTED BY:
Feldheim Publishers
POB 43163 / Jerusalem, Israel
208 Airport Executive Park
Nanuet, NY 10954
www.feldheim.com

DISTRIBUTED IN EUROPE BY:
Lehmanns
+44-0-191-430-0333
info@lehmanns.co.uk
www.lehmanns.co.uk

DISTRIBUTED IN AUSTRALIA BY:
Golds World of Judaica
+613 95278775
info@golds.com.au
www.golds.com.au

Printed in Israel

"There are people of **colors** and there are people of **sound**. There are people of **warmth** and people of **touch**. There are people of **mind** and people of **heart**. There are people of **understanding** and people of **speech**. Each of us stands out in something from the list.

"But when you find people who are both of colors and also of sound, also of understanding and also of speech, also of mind and also of heart—these are **special people** it's very worth your while to get as close to as possible."

—"The Dovecote," p. 18–19

These words describe perfectly my beloved, unforgettable firstborn son

Meir Tzvi (Tzviki) Walder, *z"l*

who passed away in the prime of his life on 21 Adar 2019 / 5779

Contents

The Dovecote

Some people can't make a move without step-
ping on someone else.
Some families can't feel good about themselves
unless they look down on others.
And when a sensitive soul grows up in an insensi-
tive family, she feels like a bird without a nest.

I grew up in a typical Brooklyn neighborhood of the 1950s.

We were about thirty Jewish families in the neighborhood, scattered among about twenty ten-story buildings.
Today, those buildings are exclusively Jewish, but back then,
there were Italians, Irish, Blacks, and only a few Jews.

We Orthodox Jews prayed together and went to Jewish
schools.

I remember Shabbos being a real highlight of the week.
Everyone went to shul—girls, too—and after services, there'd be
a *kiddush*. It was a wonderful time of prayer and togetherness.

I was an independent, opinionated girl, and very mature for

9

my age. A good student, I looked to books to explain the world around me.

I had two older brothers. As a little girl, I enjoyed looking out the front window and watching them play.

Boys' games in America were, and still are, very physical. Take football, for example. If you ask me, besides getting a lot of hard knocks, there's not much to the game. At least, that's how it looks to me. They talk about strategies like how to move the ball down the field, but what you see in front of you is boys running and crashing into each other, then picking themselves up and doing it all over again.

My brothers and their friends thought it was a great sport; to me, it was funny.

There was one boy, Ari, who played occasionally but was clearly less violent and less aggressive than the others. He was a friendly kid who talked a lot and tried to keep everyone on good terms with each other.

Tried, I said. Because trying is one thing, and making it happen is another.

He didn't succeed at it. Never. In retrospect, I don't know if it was because he didn't know how or because the kids didn't want anyone spoiling their fun of fighting. More than anything, though, I think it was his family status that decided his fate.

Even then, back in the 1950s, the dollar was king. People who had money were at the top of the social hierarchy, and the ones who didn't, weren't.

Ari's family didn't.

Not that anyone spoke against them or ostracized them, G-d forbid. They were members of the synagogue, the boys studied with my brothers, and the girls studied with me. As a matter of fact, as young kids, we didn't notice a thing.

I think I was in my teens when I realized Ari's family wasn't on a par with all the rest. No one invited them for a Shabbos meal, which was a common practice in our crowd. Everyone hosted and visited—except them. Which was strange, because they lived right across the street from us. Yet we never invited them to drop by. The relationship consisted of exchanging hellos, and that was it.

One day it dawned on me that my family disdained Ari's family. I wasn't sure how it worked or what exactly it meant. It wasn't that anyone said anything. It was more the body language of my father and brothers—the shrug of a shoulder, a raised eyebrow, a wink, a shift of gaze upward to look at an imaginary point in the sky.

That's how it was in our family. I have no idea what level it reached in other families.

The fact that Ari delivered newspapers and mowed lawns around the neighborhood clinched it. He and his family were too lower class for our snobbish families.

Once and only once did we see Ari express himself forcefully. It was when we were younger, and the city decided to remove the dovecote some kids had built in a big tree near his house.

The children didn't like the municipality's decision one bit. They crowded around the tree protectively and got their parents involved to prevent the decree from being carried out. But you can't fight city hall. When it comes to the law, sentimentality doesn't play a role. If there's a decision to cut down a tree, it gets cut down, and that's how it goes.

Ari thought differently, though. He climbed way up high in the tree and refused to allow the city workers to reach the dove-cote. They were afraid to make a move lest Ari fall and his parents sue them.

The workers stood there trying to get him to come down, but Ari wasn't having any of it. Hours passed that way until finally, their workday ended. Ari stayed up there another couple of hours until it got dark, and only then did he come down from the tree.

At first, his barricading himself like that excited the other children. He was their hero who had saved the dovecote. First thing in the morning, Ari was back up in the tree again, and nothing would get him down. Even when the police arrived, Ari just stayed up there, guarding the kids' dovecote.

This should have made Ari's status go sky-high, but it didn't turn out that way. On the third day, the children laughed at him. You could see someone had put them up to it, turning their admiration into mockery and ridicule.

But Ari didn't give up his vigil and continued to guard the children's dovecote.

Today, I know who was behind the change of attitude, but at the time, I was clueless. I remember how strange it seemed to me. We all cared about the dovecote—every single kid in the neighborhood—and we all wanted to save it. If a different kid, one with a higher social status, had climbed the tree to protect it like Ari was, that kid's status would have skyrocketed, and every kid in the neighborhood would have climbed right up there with him. But the kid protecting the dovecote was Ari, and the possibility that Ari's status might rise must have bothered a few people.

A few mocking remarks, a few smirks, a few knowing winks and raised eyebrows, and Ari turned from a heroic figure into a weird kid who barricaded himself in trees. Suddenly, the dovecote didn't matter to the kids as much as laughing at Ari for climbing the tree to protect it. They just stood there jeering, calling him a "monkey" and other names. I remember watching and feeling confused.

But that's what the kids decided, and that was it. I didn't know then that I was watching a perfect example of herd mentality. As an adult, it's easy to see how it works. A few leaders of public opinion can easily make millions of people admire something they should really despise—and despise something they should admire.

As an adult, it's easy for me to spot this type of thing, especially in politics. Back then, it was just Ari and his dovecote.

Despite everything, Ari seemed to have won. The workers stopped coming, and a well-connected community activist said the municipality had given up trying to remove the dovecote. He said the workers had told their bosses the dovecote was solidly built and strongly attached, and so did not pose a danger to anyone.

The news raised Ari's status in the children's eyes, and the dovecote regained its status as a prime neighborhood attraction. Once again, Ari was way up there—literally and figuratively.

But not for long.

One morning, when the children were in school, municipal workers came and dismantled the dovecote.

The children who'd been so proud of Ari, the boy who had saved their dovecote, turned on him and rejoiced at his downfall. Suddenly, the dovecote meant nothing to them. It was his, not theirs. They bubbled over with talk of how the municipality had played a good trick on Ari, waiting a few days to make sure he was at school and couldn't guard the dovecote before they swooped in and carted it away.

The children should have been mad at the municipality, but someone made sure to twist their anger into rejoicing.

Ari took the dovecote's disappearance badly. He withdrew into himself, which gave the kids more to laugh about. In our house, I sensed a certain cheerfulness in my brothers. It was gloating. Unfortunately, I'd gotten used to those kinds of emotions. My family, in case you haven't realized it by now, was the type in which such emotions dominated.

I might have also turned out like that—condescending and mocking—if my grandmother hadn't come to live with us when I was fifteen. I was very close to her, more than to anyone else in the world.

She had been widowed ten years earlier and never considered remarriage. She was adamant that she'd never find anyone like my grandfather.

She'd sit on the porch most of the day, watching the world pass by. She didn't talk much and never interfered with what was going on in the house. She must have been smart enough to know that having a mother-in-law living in the home could upset its balance, and she made sure it never happened. Our lives continued as always.

One day, my grandmother and I were sitting looking out the window. We saw Ari mowing the lawn across the street. My brother made some kind of a wisecrack about him, and everyone burst out laughing. The truth is, I laughed, too.

My grandmother was the only one there who made no response. Her silence cut the laughter like a knife.

The living room slowly emptied out until finally, it was just my grandmother and me.

She sat there in silence, and suddenly, I saw a tear roll down her cheek.

And then another…and another.

I wanted to ask her why she was crying, but I didn't. I sort of knew what she'd say.

"I hope you marry someone like that someday," she said suddenly.

What?! I was speechless. Shocked. Where had that come from? It was so disconnected from anything that I had no way of dealing with it.

And that's how it stayed. It raised a gnawing question: Why, out of all the boys in the neighborhood, did my grandmother like Ari the best?

And so we grew up. Ari went to an out-of-town yeshivah and came home once a month, while my brothers went to an established yeshivah, considered tops. What remained the same was my brothers' scorn for Ari and his family.

It actually seemed like the men in our family enjoyed the feeling of disdain. It seemed to make them feel good. Maybe thinking of themselves as better than someone else was the only way they could feel good.

But my grandmother never stopped thinking the world of Ari. She once told me, "He reminds me of Grandpa Nathan."

She was talking about her husband, who, to me, was "Grandpa Nathan." As I said, she never remarried because not for a minute did she think she'd find anyone who came close.

You see, Grandpa Nathan was different from our family.

Our family was arrogant and proud, while he, though wealthy and prominent, was a warm, kind man who loved others.

All of a sudden, the contrast struck me. He was exactly what our family wasn't. I'd never seen love of one's fellow man in our house. I saw a love of achievement, money, and even courage and determination, but love for other human beings was definitely not one of my family's virtues. Maybe even the opposite. There was a lot of criticism, a lot of sarcasm, and plenty of words as sharp as a knife. The other person was always someone who was jealous of us or wanted our downfall, and we had to show everyone that we were worth more than others, so no one would look down on us.

That's how we'd grown up. I think lots of people in our neighborhood felt the same way, going by the condescending way they acted. On the outside, all you could see were smiles. But inside, there was suspicion, competitiveness, and a lot of fear of other people.

Suddenly, I realized what an important role Ari's family played. They were everything we weren't.

They were always inferior to us, at least in our eyes. Unlike our subtle competitiveness with the other families in the neighborhood, we had no problem with them. There was no competition at all. Next to them, my family could just sit back with folded arms and laugh at them without a single concern that they might have something worth more than we did.

If you want to understand why some people are racist and condescending, I think the situation in our neighborhood gave me a great understanding of that. I would sum it up in one sentence: Racism and condescension are the easiest ways a person can feel superior without any effort.

Looking back, I wonder how I survived growing up in such a house. So it's like this: Our house was divided into three. Some were strong and cynical, like my father and two of my brothers. Nobody started up with them. They dominated. My sister and I just sat there quietly, trying not to get into their line of fire. And if by mistake, we did get in their sights, or if someone decided out of the blue to hurt us because he didn't have anything better to do, we just lowered our heads until the storm passed.

There were two people in the house who did not take things quietly but were also not strong enough mentally to stand up to this wall of cynicism. They were damaged and suffered emotionally from it.

The first was one of my brothers who fell between the cracks and suffered from the verbal abuse in the house. He paid an emotional price for it, which I prefer not to talk about.

The second was my mother. She suffered in her own way. She had an easygoing personality, but at times she was forced to set limits. I think she kind of sacrificed herself to protect us, even from ourselves.

And then there was Grandma, who knew full well that if she intervened, it would only make things worse, so she remained silent.

Yet for this guy, Ari, she broke her silence. Not to everyone. Just to me.

One day, Grandma went over and knocked on the door of our neighbors, Ari's parents. We didn't know about it right away, but at some point, we realized with a shock that our grandmother was becoming friendly with Ari's family.

In our house, no one knew what to make of it. At first, they ignored it, as if that would mean it wasn't happening. But when the relationship became permanent and public, we could no longer ignore it. My brothers started with their cynical comments, which I won't repeat.

I was torn. My family's brainwashing against Ari's family was very powerful. It didn't matter what you really thought. If I ever dared say anything besides the party line, I'd be so put down and mocked that I feared for my mental health. So I just kept quiet.

On the other hand...

On the other hand, there was my silent, noble grandmother, who hardly spoke, but when it came to these neighbors, she sprang to life and spoke with such admiration that it really made me jealous.

One day I asked her, "Grandma, why are you so enthusiastic about that family? Why are you so excited about this guy who delivers newspapers and mows lawns?"

"He also sells the four species before Succos and puts away the *sefarim* in shul."

I didn't say anything. My question still hung there.

"Let me ask you a question," she said to me. "How is his learning? Did you investigate how well liked he is in his yeshivah? Have you noticed how many people count on him in the neighborhood? Do you see how much the children, the adults, and the elderly admire and appreciate him?"

"I saw the adults," I said cynically, "but the teens not so much."

"You mean the teenage boys who live in *this* house."

I never dreamed she knew how to be cynical, too.

One day I saw Ari climb to the top floor of an apartment building to open the door for an elderly woman who was stuck outside. My grandmother went outside, as did some of the other residents of the neighborhood. I came down, too. Everyone crowded around him, thanking him for what he'd done. He flushed with embarrassment and disappeared as soon as he politely could.

When I walked my grandmother home, she said, "There are people of colors and there are people of sound. There are people of warmth and people of touch. There are people of mind and people of heart. There are people of understanding and people of speech. Each of us stands out in something from the list.

"But when you find people who are both of colors and also of sound, also of understanding and also of speech, also of mind and also of heart—these are special people it's very worth your while to get as close as possible to."

My breath caught. These were magical words I'd never heard before. Certainly not from my quiet grandmother.

"Grandpa Nathan was one of those," she said. "He shone on me so much that to this day, I am still filled with his light. I don't want to get married again because I'm afraid anyone else would only make a shadow instead of the light I have."

That's what Grandma told me, and it was the longest speech she ever gave me. And the deepest.

We grew up. I turned twenty. My brothers married girls from families like ours, snobby and painfully rich, proud of their very presence in the world.

When it was my turn, somehow, we got stuck. I couldn't find what I wanted, and so I got older, and it came about that while all my brothers and sisters were already married, I wasn't. I was approaching thirty.

Then someone from the neighborhood suggested Ari. My father laughed out loud and said there was nothing to talk about.

At first, the idea sounded crazy to me, but as the days, weeks, and months passed, and the more I talked to my grandmother, I realized that this was the man I'd been looking for from the start. All my trying to run away from it hadn't helped. He was there waiting for me all the time.

I told the matchmaker I was willing to give it a try. He brought in the Rav of our shul and told my father to at least let us try. But my father was strongly opposed and got my brothers and sister to try getting me to drop the idea. For them, it would be humiliating for someone from our family to make a *shidduch* with a family they'd enjoyed putting down their whole lives.

People from the community came and spoke with them. When my father saw that my mother and I were determined to go through with it, and the community supported us, he sent one of my brothers to talk to Ari.

Everyone breathed a sigh of relief—finally, a crack in the wall of resistance.

But they were wrong because right after my brother talked to Ari, Ari told the matchmaker he was dropping the idea. He said he didn't want to marry a girl from our family.

I was so hurt I cried for a few days straight. I was mad, too. I wanted to know what my brother had told Ari to make him drop the *shidduch*. My brother refused to say a word.

Nowadays, in that situation, I'd make inquiries. But back then, things were different. People, especially women, hesitated to express their opinion.

I used to sit with Grandma, and she would sigh loudly. She was already quite old, quickly approaching her twilight years. But what was between us was between us.

And then, one day, as we sat looking out the window, she told me, "I know what Grandpa Nathan would do."

"What he would do about what?" I asked.

"About your *shidduch*. We both know that Ari is perfect for you. He's your *bashert*, and the only thing keeping you from your true happiness is a wall of pride and snobbery. If anyone had tried to keep me apart like that from Nathan, I know just what he would have done."

When she didn't continue, I asked her, "What would he have done?"

She whispered a few words in my ear. It was the strangest idea I'd ever heard.

"Why would Grandpa Nathan do such a thing?" I asked her.

"Think it over, and you'll understand on your own without me telling you," she said.

Grandma had just told me something very strange, as if assuming I knew why Ari decided to drop the *shidduch*. Or perhaps it was her way of telling me what I wasn't supposed to know.

I decided to ask my mother. I knew my grandmother wouldn't have said what she'd said out of the blue. There must have been a reason. And that reason must have something to do with the fact that the boy said no.

It took some persuasion, but I finally got my mother to tell me how my brother convinced Ari to drop the *shidduch*.

"He told Ari it wouldn't be a good idea for him to join our family because everyone in it hates him. And since everyone hates him, in the end, his wife, who was supposed to be you, will also hate him. He said he has nothing to look for from us, he's not our type, and a marriage that begins like this can only end in divorce."

"So what if they told him that? Is that what turned him off? He was insulted?"

"No," my mother replied. "It wasn't the insult that kept Ari away. Not at all. On the contrary, Ari answered him calmly and said he thought things would work out over time. Once he was given a chance, he'd get along with everyone.

"Then," my mother said, "your brother told Ari something that convinced him in an instant to pick himself up and run away from our family."

I looked at her in horror. "What could he possibly have said?"

"He told him the big secret we've kept all these years, a secret even you don't know about."

"What did he tell him?!" I almost shouted.

"Well, your brother said to him like this, 'Do you remember your dovecote? The one you protected by sitting up in the tree for two days? You probably wonder to this day who took it. Remember how everyone told you it was workers from the municipality? That's what they said, but it wasn't true. I'll tell you what really happened. One day, my brothers and I left school an hour after it began. My dad had given us a note asking permission for us to be released for "a family matter." You know what the "family matter" was? I'm going to tell you. We came home, and there was my father waiting for us with special equipment. We climbed the tree, dismantled your dovecote, and threw the pieces into an empty lot in another neighborhood. Now do you understand why you shouldn't marry into our family? We've already broken up one nest of yours. It'll be nothing for us to break up the nest you want to build for yourself.'

"Ari didn't need to hear more than that," my mother told me. "That was enough for him to get the full picture of just who he was dealing with. Ari told your brother straight out, 'You're right. You just convinced me. You really are a family of wicked people. You can be sure I won't go anywhere near this *shidduch*.'"

She told me they shook hands on it like gentlemen who'd made a good deal. I was the only one who lost out.

That's how, with a few words, I lost the man of the mind and heart, understanding and speech.

That's what my mother told me, and I didn't know what to cry for more. For having a family like this? For growing up in a home as cold as the North Pole and as burning hot as

Gehinnom? For losing the best guy I could ever get, a perfect guy like Grandpa Nathan?

At that very moment, my grandmother's strange advice came to mind, and I knew I was going to do it, just like Grandpa Nathan would have.

One bright morning, a truck drove into our neighborhood. Workers arrived and, on that ancient tree that stood between Ari's house and ours, built the most beautiful dovecote people in our neighborhood had ever seen.

It took everyone time to hear about it, but eventually, they did. Heads peered out of windows, and then people came outside and looked.

I went out there with my grandmother. She was sitting in her wheelchair, and I stood there, telling the workers how to best position the dovecote. And with perfect timing, just as the workers finished their job, a van arrived with the birds, and the man delivering the doves placed them in the dovecote.

It took a while, but in the end, everyone realized it wasn't just a dovecote. It was a gesture. And they began to whisper.

They remembered very well the boy who barricaded himself up in the tree and prevented the municipality from taking the dovecote. Some even knew who'd really taken it. They realized that the new dovecote had come to right a wrong. But none of them knew the big message behind building this dovecote.

A couple of days later, the original matchmaker was sent to Ari's parents to suggest the *shidduch* again. He didn't even have to explain what he wanted. There was a clear statement here that answered all of Ari's questions.

Ari said yes.

I consulted with the neighborhood Rav, and at his suggestion, I informed my father that I'd decided to marry Ari. My father didn't react. He just nodded and said, "I'll respect your decision."

I think he didn't want his thirty-year-old daughter sitting at home until her hair turned gray.

My brothers didn't see any choice but to go along with it, and I got married a few months later.

Dozens of years have passed since then. My grandmother died four years after the wedding. Over the years, my father and mother also passed away. Somehow, it turned out that I was the one who inherited their home, where Ari and I raised our five children and to which we welcome our grandchildren and great-grandchildren.

To this day, we sit on the porch looking at the tree and the old dovecote that's still there. Ari, who eventually won over every single member of my family, from my siblings to the last of their descendants, likes to say, "This dovecote should remain right where it is forever. Let it serve as a symbol to all our descendants of how people can destroy their lives with arrogance and snobbery. It will teach them how bad *middos* can destroy a dovecote and how good *middos* can rebuild it. And besides," he adds with a twinkle in his eye, "it will also remind them about who proposed to whom."

"Move the Car Already!"

A pair of playful criminals find their way to the right path in a very strange way.

They are sent to make a "persuasive call" close to Shabbos and discover that their car is blocked by a parked car.

Typically, their kind of people has no problem getting anyone they want to move their vehicle.

But this time they meet up with a very special client.

My story took place thirty-five years ago. No one other than the people directly involved knows about it, and when you read what happened, you'll understand why.

I was born and raised in a neighborhood that wasn't one of the best, to put it mildly. You once wrote that 20 percent of the children in a normal society may get into trouble in their teenage years. Well, my neighborhood wasn't exactly what you'd call normal. It was a poverty-stricken neighborhood. Or, to be more accurate, a crime-ridden neighborhood. I think about 70 percent of the kids got into trouble either with the police or in other ways. Some of them are still in trouble until this very day, and some are no longer in trouble because they've gone Upstairs in all kinds of unnatural ways.

Let's skip my childhood and teenage years and go straight to when I was twenty-four.

I worked for a man whose name frequently appeared in the headlines, and not because of the mitzvos he did or the money he donated to charity. He was a criminal. He sat in prison a few times, and everyone who worked for him was automatically suspect and frequently stopped by the police either for questioning or as a warning.

Why did I work for him? Because, as a kid who never liked school, I saw working for him as the only way to get ahead in life. Deep down, I knew working for him was a risky business that put me in constant danger—the greater your seniority, the lower your life expectancy. Let's just say that no insurance company in the world would insure guys like me, even for a premium the size of a monthly salary.

At twenty-four, though, I was still considered a novice and wasn't assigned missions with no way out.

One Friday, I went with a friend to a big city, which will remain nameless.

We were supposed to collect money from someone, and if you ask why our boss didn't go through legal channels to get what was coming to him, the answer is that he didn't want to bother the courts with his affairs. They were busy enough as it was. What's more, he knew it was easier to get a delinquent tenant to pay back rent than to get money owed by this particular customer. So he sent us, in particular my friend, who was called Mordy "Fuhgeddaboudit," whose very appearance sent a strong message to the client that our boss was anxious to see results. Or else.

Actually, as you might have guessed, Mordy's last name was not "Fuhgeddaboudit." His real last name was known by only the select few, among them his parents and siblings. The name "Fuhgeddaboudit" stuck to him because of his habit of speaking harshly to others. Whenever he encountered even the slightest reluctance to go along with one of his "suggestions," he'd say, "You know what? Fuhgeddaboudit."

When Mordy said "Fuhgeddaboudit," for some reason, no one forgot about it, maybe because something in his tone of voice suggested dire consequences if they dared forget about it. In fact, when Mordy said "Fuhgeddaboudit," for some reason, people got the impression that they should *remember* and *even memorize* what Mordy was saying and do exactly as he said.

As I mentioned, it was Friday. When I say Friday, I'm talking about late afternoon heading toward evening.

We parked the car near a shul and walked to the client's house. We got there and knocked, but the guy didn't open the door. Mordy leaned on the door a little, and it opened. Then we sat down with the man of the house, drank some water with him, and spoke with him "nicely." Let me just say that Mordy Fuhgeddaboudit's "nice" way of talking is not the type of speech you want to encounter in a dark alley. Or even a lit one.

We ended the courtesy call and left, after having collected what we came for.

As we neared the spot where we'd parked the car, we saw

that someone had parked right behind us, blocking us. Mordy and I had no chance of getting out of our spot unless the owner of the car moved it.

Usually, such matters end in a simple way. Mordy locates the car owner, lets loose with a few hair-raising shouts at how dare he block such a busy man and who did he think he was, and the panicked fellow races to move his car and let Mordy out.

The same was true even when Mordy parked his car in the reserved parking spot of an innocent, law-abiding citizen, who had that spot registered as his private property.

Apparently, there is a tendency for those same citizens to resent it when they see someone else's car sitting in their driveway. Some of them get pretty upset about it and make a lot of trouble, which begins by blocking the parked vehicle and ends with checking the tires to see if they remain inflated after they've been slashed with a watermelon knife. My thinking is that this test is completely unnecessary, because it's been tried many times before over the years, and the results are always the same. However, some of those parking spot owners insist on treating each case like it's unique.

They quickly unblock the offending car when they meet up with a serial parking offender named Mordy "Fuhgeddaboudit," because they soon learn that there are two sides to the coin or the tire or the shattered mirror. Suddenly, they're anxious to offer occasional "guest parking," or at least to check the identity of said guests to see whether they're the type to accept the verdict with love and drive away with an apologetic murmur—or whether they're like Mordy "Fuhgeddaboudit," from whom a glance is all it takes for the parking spot owner to abandon his plans, or, simply put, to "fuhgeddaboudit."

To be honest, I know of an incident where Mordy smashed two BMW side mirrors. And when I asked him why one wasn't enough, he explained to me that, "I was only going to take out one, but when I kicked it, it hurt my leg, and I got mad. To get back at the first mirror, I took out the second. The owner of the car isn't really to blame for the second one."

After this long description of Mordy Fuhgeddaboudit's complex relationship with cars that block him, I return to that particular car that was blocking Mordy and me near the shul that Friday night.

Mordy asked one of the children playing near the shul, "Whose car is this?"

"I don't know," a boy said. "He prays here, but he's new."

Mordy entered the shul, put one hand on his head, and whispered, "Whose car is that outside? Move it!"

Everyone turned to look at Mordy, but it didn't occur to Mordy that there was a flaw in his request, namely that it was already Shabbos. Although Mordy hadn't found out earlier when Shabbos began or ended, still, he should have known that not a single person in that shul was going to move a car right then even if his life depended on it.

But as you've surely realized by now, Mordy wasn't the most understanding type of person. And when no one made a move to fulfill his request, what did he do if not shout out loud, "Skoda with license plate number 32322801, *move your car*! If not, I'm slashing the tires!"

Guess what?

No one moved—and certainly, no one made a move to move the car.

"Whose car is it?!" Mordy demanded.

Everyone was silent. Apparently, they'd all been stricken by an attack of forgetfulness. One of them explained to him that because Shabbos had begun an hour earlier, there was no way anyone would move the car.

When Mordy realized there was absolutely no chance of anyone moving the car blocking his, he shouted, "You know what? Fuhgeddaboudit!"

Mordy left in a rage, opened the trunk, and took out the most valuable object in it, at least according to his worldview—the baseball bat he occasionally used to convince stubborn people.

The next step was going to be smashing the taillights and then waiting. After that, he'd move on to the headlights and then wait again. Then he'd move to the windows. How did I know? Come on.

When he neared the right taillight, his favorite starting point, a little girl with braids went up to him and said, "What's wrong?"

We looked at the girl and saw she had Down syndrome. From the way she said, "What's wrong?" we knew it was because she cared. But frankly, even if she'd said it as a criticism, Mordy wouldn't have minded because he has respect for cute little girls with Down syndrome. He explained to the girl that he wanted to play baseball but he couldn't find a ball right then, so he was a little worried.

"We have a ball," the girl told him and ran off to bring him the ball. She was back in a flash and threw the ball straight at Mordy's baseball bat. Mordy had no choice but to restore the bat to its original purpose—to play ball. From here on in, an interesting game developed between Mordy and the little girl with braids.

People came out of the shul and went on their way. One of them took the little girl by the hand, and Mordy was left without a partner for the game, which brought him back to the major problem he had to deal with. Someone was blocking his car.

We leaned on the car, and Mordy said, "I know what I'll do. I'll call the police."

If he had said he was taking an electric bicycle and riding to the moon, it would have sounded a lot *less* strange than the words "I'll call the police," because, for Mordy, the police are a group that *makes* problems, not solves them. But Mordy seemed to be feeling down, and you can guess why. What do you think he did if not call the police to notify them that a car was blocking him?

In cases like that, the police will call the owner of the car to tell him to move his vehicle. But guess what? The car owner didn't answer the call from the police.

"Sorry, Mister," the policeman said, "but the owner of the car isn't answering."

"So send a patrol car," Mordy said.

Half an hour later, a patrol car drove up. Two policemen got out to check the situation. Mordy spoke to them nicely, invented a story about a sick grandmother or something like that, and asked them to tell him who the owner was.

The police explained that according to the law, they are not allowed to tell him who the car belonged to, but they knew the owner's address, and they'd drive over to him and wake him up to move his car.

It was clear to us that the odds of the car owner moving his vehicle were just about equal to the odds of him being asleep at that moment instead of sitting with his family and singing Shabbos songs. However, we said nothing to the policemen about this viewpoint since it might convince them not to go to the family's house, which would fundamentally disrupt Mordy's plan.

The cops drove off, and Mordy and I went up to a nearby roof to see where they went.

Since police vehicles have flashing blue-and-white lights on the roof, they're easy to track. As soon as the patrol car stopped, Mordy and I ran in the approximate direction, and soon we were standing not far from the building in front of which it had stopped.

I walked into the building to see which floor the cops had climbed to, and then we both hid nearby.

Sure enough, we got a call a few minutes later. The policeman regretfully informed us that the car owner was a Sabbath-observant man who had driven to the shul several minutes before Shabbos and parked in his usual parking spot. Apparently, he refused to move the car or even give the car keys to the police. They were sorry and suggested we come back after Shabbos was over.

Mordy thanked them and said he'd already left the shul area and would make an effort to work things out on his own.

In doing so, Mordy surprisingly told the truth. We really had left the shul area, and our intentions *were* to make an effort to work things out on our own—with an emphasis on the word *effort*.

The patrol car left the area, and our feet took us up to the third floor, to the home of the driver and his family. The information, in case you didn't get it, was courtesy of the police force.

I must point out that Mordy had taken nothing from his car except the baseball bat.

We knocked, and a few seconds later, the door was opened by the man of the house who apparently realized very quickly who we were and what we had come for.

To be honest, his eyes widened in surprise. He thought that

with the departure of the police, the matter was over and done with. It hadn't occurred to him that it was just beginning.

"I'll make it short," Mordy said. "I understand you're not willing to move your car on Shabbat, and I can even respect that. But right now you are going to bring me the keys to the car and give me the code. I'll move it, move mine out, and return yours to the parking spot."

Mordy held out his hand, palm up. Like me, he was sure that in less than a minute, the keys would be there.

"The police were here," the man said calmly, "and they threatened to arrest me and give me a fine, and now you came. I have absolutely nothing against you, but I'm not going to give you the keys until the minute Shabbos is over. I promise, though, to give you special consideration. Even though I keep Rabbeinu Tam time, I won't make you wait that long. I'll make sure the keys are in your hands right after Shabbos ends, but not a minute earlier."

I didn't look at him but at Mordy. I saw him pursing his lips tightly, a sure sign he was unhappy with recent developments. The vein in his neck was bulging on the side that wielded the bat.

"Fuhgeddaboudit," Mordy said to him. "I'll just take care of your car now."

"*Shabbat shalom,*" the man said as if he'd been told good news.

"Did you hear what I just said?!" Mordy shouted. From inside, we could hear the sound of children crying.

"You told me to fuhgeddaboudit, and that's exactly what I'm going to do."

Now Mordy was trapped. True, he'd made a threat, but for some reason, it hadn't had its usual effect. Then again, he really had said, "Fuhgeddaboudit," so he couldn't really punish the guy for taking him at his word.

"You know what?" Mordy said. "Forget what I said. I won't hurt your car, I'll hurt *you*." He raised the bat.

The man looked like someone really anxious about meeting up with a baseball bat, and I was willing to bet he'd met up with one before. As for myself, I preferred not to meet up with a baseball bat due to my first and only meeting with one at the age of eighteen. That bat was not held by Mordy but by a skinny boy my age who almost collapsed under its weight. Also, Mordy had various ways of preventing damage to his bat's smooth surface, such as sticking nails in it. That's why I was genuinely amazed at the chareidi man's determination when faced with the raised baseball bat, decorated with a crown of steel, held by Mordy.

"It's written in the *sefarim*," the man said calmly, "about the holy *Tanna* Rabbi Akiva that when they combed his flesh with iron combs, he said the Shema. And when his students asked him, 'To such an extent?' he told them, 'All my life when I said *bechol nafshecha* in the Shema I knew that the meaning of those words is "even if they take your life." But I've never had a chance to prove it. Now, when I have the chance to fulfill this, shouldn't I do so joyfully?'

"I, too, have kept Shabbos my whole life without being tested," the man told us, "and now that a test has been sent my way, should I give in? No, just the opposite. So do what you want to me."

"A test was sent your way, huh?!" Mordy roared and lifted the baseball bat.

Suddenly, a voice said, "Did you lose your ball again? Wait a sec. I'll bring you one."

Yes, it was the cute little girl with braids.

Naturally, Mordy was not about to hit anyone standing right next to someone with Down syndrome or any other syndrome for that matter. I watched as his angry face changed into a fake smile, and even that vein in his neck disappeared.

"I really don't have a ball," he said to the girl with braids, "and I was wondering if you had one."

"Sure. Here," she said, and suddenly threw him a ball. Because Mordy wasn't expecting it, the ball bounced off his head.

Let me just say there was something unsportsmanlike about this surprise she gave him—and Mordy did not usually remain silent when faced with unsportsmanlike actions, especially since he's a big believer in sportsmanship. But nothing was usual about this situation, and Mordy didn't actually play sports, so... Besides, the opposing player wasn't exactly the type you could complain about to a sports association. Therefore, Mordy had to admit defeat and quickly hit the second ball she threw at him if he didn't want to get a reputation for getting hit and failing to hit back.

I also noticed that he made sure that contact between the ball and the bat was on the side without nails because we have strict rules when it comes to destroying balls belonging to girls with braids and Down syndrome.

After a short game, he told the girl the game was over, and then hissed to her father, "You got out of it for now, but tomorrow I'll be there waiting for you at the shul."

We left the place, and there was no doubt that Mordy was upset. For the first time in his life, he had to leave his car blocked by a stranger.

We walked down the street like two losers beaten by a single adversary who, according to all the rules, should have begged

Mordy to take the car keys and even the car itself. But the man we'd met didn't play by our rules.

"I have to make my point," Mordy said to me. "The guy was saved because of the little girl, but now my bat is disappointed, and I have to use it to hit that rude dude's car."

We walked to where we'd left our car. I wondered if I should tell him it might make the little girl sad, but I decide not to share my viewpoint with Mordy for fear he would forget about the car and turn his attention to me.

We were about a hundred yards from a meeting between the baseball bat and the taillights when suddenly we heard a loud and terrifying blast. The blast knocked us both to the ground, and even before we could stand up, we saw flames of fire shooting up from where our car was parked.

We ran to the spot, where we were joined by a few dozen adults, teens, and kids. We were soon facing the remnants of what used to be our car and discovered that its front half, where we would have been sitting, was completely destroyed. Miraculously, the back of the car remained intact, except for the glass that took the opportunity to fly away. No one needed to explain to us what had happened: Several hours earlier, someone had planted a powerful bomb under our car, right where we would have been sitting. It was set to go off when, according to schedule, we would be on our way up north—if some religious guy hadn't had the chutzpah to block us.

Of course, this insight fundamentally changed Mordy's negative thoughts about that religious guy who'd had the nerve to stand up to him, and also made him immediately drop all plans to wreck the guy's car, which miraculously remained untouched, with the exception of one broken window on the left.

Several minutes later, we realized that the fire department would alert the police, who might ask questions whose answers could complicate our lives to a certain degree. Therefore, we decided to make ourselves scarce until the coast was clear. The people who went to so much trouble to surprise us with a car bomb for our trip probably didn't like us all that much, and when they found out we hadn't been in that car, they just might conclude that we were still alive and come to further conclusions as to their future actions.

We left instructions where we needed to leave instructions and went into hiding. By Sunday, the attempt to eliminate us was front-page news in all the newspapers.

In the first few hours after the explosion, I discovered that Mordy and I were on the same page. Both of us had a vivid mental image of what would have happened if the man had given us the car keys. No doubt about it. Doing that would have significantly lowered our life expectancy from eighty-two to twenty-four. No matter how you look at it, that's a significant reduction in a basic consumer good called life. Mordy, like me, came to the conclusion that one thing had kept him alive and not rising to the skies together with an ordinary C-4 car bomb, and that one thing was nothing but Shabbos, or, to be precise, the man who guarded it.

He and a little girl with braids.

Guess what Mordy did next?

He entered a famous yeshivah for *baalei teshuvah* and started to learn.

And guess who went right along with him?

We did worry that our boss would get mad about our decision to quit our jobs (though in doing so we were giving up pensions and sick leave, which anyway don't exist in that line of work). But it turned out that when they check and see that you really decided to do *teshuvah*, they don't touch you. It's an unwritten law similar to the one that bans certain baseball bat activities near cute little girls with Down syndrome.

The bottom line? Within two years, Mordy and I both married and established fully *chareidi* homes.

All of our friends, without exception, found themselves in prison or in the grave or both, except those who did *teshuvah* like us.

Thirty-five years have passed since then. We've both already raised children and have grandchildren.

I'm still in contact with Mordy. It's unbelievable what doing *teshuvah* did for him. Where is the violence, the anger, the threats?

Fuhgeddaboudit.

A few weeks ago, Mordy and I decided to go back to visit that *chareidi* man.

We climbed the stairs to his apartment, knocked, and told him who we were. He hadn't known what became of us, but he'd realized at the time that we'd been saved because of his stand on keeping Shabbos. He told us he'd often wondered if we'd learned anything from it. Now he had his answer.

"Please forgive me for those moments when I threatened you," Mordy said to him.

"There's no need," he replied. "I cherish the memory of those moments because they gave my children a vivid demonstration of just how important Shabbos is, to the extent that I was even ready to suffer bodily harm to keep it."

And then, a modestly dressed woman gracefully entered the living room and gave a big Down syndrome smile.

"She's still with us," her father said with a smile of his own. "Everyone else got married and brought us grandchildren, but she will always be with us."

We sat there and cried because we knew that this woman, who was once a cute little girl with braids, had saved our souls.

And along with her, Shabbos had saved our lives.

(Not) By Chance

The protagonist feels ill and is rushed to the hospital.

There he meets a man who seems distraught.

Politeness dictates that he not get involved. He doesn't...until his wife forces him to.

Between the two options lies a distance of two fingers.

Six years ago, late one night, I suddenly felt overwhelming nausea. I figured I must have eaten something that disagreed with me. It can happen, can't it? No big deal.

But vomiting blood in the middle of the night is a very big deal.

It was 1:00 a.m. I didn't know who to turn to. The first name that came to mind was our family doctor, but I'd never called him at home before, and certainly not after midnight.

"Let it ring twice," my wife suggested. "I think he'll understand how worried you are."

I made the call.

Luckily, he answered after the first ring.

After I described the problem, he said, "Go to the emergency room immediately."

I asked no questions.

My wife and I drove to the hospital.

At first, the EMTs seemed very worried and did a lot of tests. But they soon concluded that it wasn't anything dangerous. Still, they wanted me to stay in the hospital for three days of observation, during which they'd run various tests to arrive at an accurate diagnosis.

My wife and I walked out of the emergency room to sit in the waiting area outside.

We weren't the only ones. Other patients were sitting there, and hospital staff passed by in a continuous stream. But as our eyes adjusted to our surroundings, one man in particular caught our attention. He looked very nervous and worried.

"That man seems very upset," my wife said a few minutes later. "Maybe you want to ask him if he needs any help?"

"What do you expect in a hospital?" I said to her. "It's a place where people *are* worried and *look* worried."

"But he seems more nervous than the average. Listen to what I'm telling you."

After a few moments of silence during which I made no move to approach the stranger, my wife quoted to me from that week's *parashah, Vayeishev*. That's the *parashah* in which Yosef notices the troubled expression of the chief cupbearer and the chief baker and asks them, "Why are your faces sad today?"

"I think it's a sign for you to ask him what's bothering him and see if you can help," my wife said.

What choice did I have?

I stood up and went over to the man. "Excuse me for inter-fering," I said to him, "but I can't help but see you're very upset about something. Is there anything I can do to help?"

"I *am* very upset," the man, who looked to be in his forties, said. "In fact, I don't remember a time in my life when I was more stressed. I'm faced with a choice, but I see no way to make the decision."

I wondered what decision he had to make. I didn't ask, but he volunteered the information.

"I have a sixteen-year-old son, and two of his fingers got cut off in a household accident. We put the fingers in ice and brought him here. After the doctors examined his hand, they told me to choose between two options.

"The first option is to leave his hand as is. He'd go through life with just three fingers on that hand. It's a disability, but he could function with it. The second option is to perform an operation to rejoin the fingers. However, the operation might jeopardize the entire palm of his hand and all five fingers. The operation carries the risk of leaving the hand completely paralyzed.

"They gave me half an hour to decide, and I'm walking around here and don't even know who to consult. I don't even have the courage to call my wife and ask her what she thinks. She'll panic and get hysterical, and that certainly won't help me make the right decision."

"You're right about one thing," I said to him. "There's no way for you to decide between the two options. And to tell you the truth, I don't have any ideas, either. But if you ask me, there is one person who can make the decision."

"Who would that be?" the man asked.

"Have you ever heard of Rabbi Elimelech Firer?"

"Sure I've heard of him," he said. "But as far as I know, it takes a few months to get through to him. What chance would a random caller have at two thirty in the morning?"

"Let me try," I suggested.

I pulled out my cellphone and called an assistant to an assistant and then another assistant to an assistant, and within a quarter of an hour, Rabbi Elimelech Firer himself was on the line.

The father was too overcome with emotion to speak, so I presented the question to Rabbi Firer. After hearing what I had to say, he asked to speak to the father directly and asked him a few more questions. He then asked him to bring the phone to one of the doctors. After speaking with a doctor, he asked to speak again with the father.

"Wait five minutes," Rabbi Firer said, "and I'll call you back at this number."

We held our breaths. Meanwhile, the man showered me with all the thanks in the world, and then the phone rang.

"This is what you need to do," Rabbi Firer said. "The operation will be done, but not in this hospital. Go to the admittance desk, get your son released from the hospital, and take him and the fingers to Assaf Harofeh hospital as fast as you can. An expert surgeon is waiting there to perform the surgery."

Then Rabbi Firer hung up.

"What should I do?" the man asked.

"You do exactly what Rabbi Firer told you to do," I said. "Get your son released and rush over there."

He took my cellphone number, and within minutes he was racing with his son to Assaf Harofeh.

Too late, I remembered I hadn't gotten his phone number.

Another hour and a half went by. Further tests I took indicated there was no cause for worry. It was something small in the esophagus that would resolve itself in a few days. My wife and I were free to go home.

We got home at four thirty in the morning.

"I think I'll stay up to daven *vasikin*," I told my wife.

Believe it or not, who did I run into at shul if not my family physician.

"Did you go to the ER?" he asked me.

"Yes," I told him. "*Baruch Hashem*, they said it's a small problem in the esophagus that will go away within a day or two."

"That's what I thought."

I smiled. "With all due respect, and I do respect you, especially since you answered the phone at 1:30 a.m., you actually thought it was urgent enough to send me running to the emergency room."

"Yes, I did," he said. "But let me tell you why. I'm usually asleep at that hour, especially since I daven *netz*. But last night I had trouble sleeping so I picked up a medical journal and read about a case where a man was vomiting blood and the doctor didn't take it that seriously and told him it would go away. He didn't know it could indicate a perforated intestine, and the patient died a couple of hours later. Right when I finished the article, the phone rang, and you were on the line telling me you vomited blood. Now you tell me, what should a believing Jew do? Doesn't it look like a message from Heaven?"

I got excited.

"It certainly was a message from Heaven," I told him. "You have no idea to what extent. But the message wasn't for me, but for a secular Jew who had no idea what to do. His sixteen-year-old son had just lost two fingers, and the doctors wanted him to decide whether they should stitch up the cuts and leave the hand with just three fingers or reattach the two fingers in an operation that risked causing permanent damage to his hand. There wasn't a single person in the world he could call for advice. But my vomiting, your insomnia, and the article you read was the message from Heaven to get me there to make the connection between him and Rabbi Firer."

We were both awed and inspired by our roles in this manifestation of Hashem's loving guidance.

I went home and told my wife.

"I wonder what happened to the boy's fingers," she said.

"We have no way of knowing," I replied. "We'll just have to wait for him to call."

A month passed, then two months, but no word from them.

I could have tried to find out through some of Rabbi's Firer's helpers and their assistants, but I decided that wasn't my job.

Three months passed, and one day my phone rang. The man from the hospital was on the line.

"Can I come over to your house?" he asked.

"Yes, certainly," I said, giving him the address.

Actually, I was a little worried. Maybe the surgery hadn't gone well, and he was angry. Maybe he was coming to take revenge. Then again, I knew that one who does a mitzvah does not come to harm because of it.

An hour later, four luxury cars pulled up in front of our building. Grandparents, the father and the mother, the boy, and assorted relatives exited. Their entire family was coming to our house.

They arrived at the door bearing a large bouquet of flowers. The man embraced me and said, "Yesterday, we got the final results. The operation was a complete success. Our son can move his fingers just like before. Here, look—he can wave with all five fingers as if two of them had never been cut off just three months ago.

"Listen to what happened," the father told us once we were all seated. "When I got to Assaf Harofeh, the surgeon was waiting for me. He asked me: 'What's your connection with Rabbi Firer that he woke me up at this time of night?'

"'I don't know him at all,' I told him. 'Like everyone else, I've heard of him. But a short time ago, I met a *chareidi* fellow in the hospital, and he asked me why I was so upset. When I told him, he spared no effort to put me in touch with Rabbi Firer. That's how I got to you.'"

Then the father added, "I gathered from the doctor that doing the surgery privately would have cost me tens of thousands of shekels. I decided that if the surgery were successful, I would give that money to you. I hope you realize that my son's fingers are worth a lot more."

He pulled out a bulging brown envelope and put it on the table.

I stared at it. "Sorry," I said to him, "but you'll have to forgive me for not taking this money. It's a great privilege to save a person's limb. I would never take money for it."

He tried to argue with me about it but as soon as he saw that not only wasn't I going to take the money, but I was even a little offended by the offer, he stopped.

Then his sixteen-year-old son surprised us all by asking for a pen and paper.

We gave it to him, and he wrote a few lines and handed it to me.

I read, "Because you saved my hand, I commit to putting

on tefillin for the rest of my life, even though we are not religious and I have never put on tefillin, not even on my bar mitzvah."

Tears welled up in my eyes, and before I knew it, I was crying openly—and I'm not that type at all.

After I'd managed to calm down, I told everyone, "This is the biggest present you could have given me or any other Jew in the world. If I came down into This World just for a Jew to put on tefillin all his life—there's no gift worth more than that. Right now, I'm the one who owes you a big thanks, not the opposite."

They saw how moved I was, and they, too, became emotional. You could see they were just as surprised as I was by their son's promise, but they went along with it 100 percent.

We said goodbye, and they left.

During the year, we had no special connection, except before the holidays, when I called to wish them well. Then my daughter got engaged, and I invited them to the wedding.

They came—though not the whole family, just the father and son. They wore yarmulkes and stayed for almost the entire wedding. Then, before they left, the father came over to me and handed me two envelopes.

"One for you," he said, "and one for the couple."

A wedding is a wedding. You're not going to refuse a wedding present. So I said thank you and put the envelopes in my inner jacket pocket.

An hour later, the wedding ended, the guests dispersed, and I went to the bandleader to give him the final payment.

"It's okay," he told me. "It's already been paid."

My conscientious mechutan must have beat me to it, I thought to myself. *I'll settle it with him later.*

Then I went to the photographer, but he told me the same thing: "Paid."

This was getting embarrassing. I ran to the wedding hall's office, opened my checkbook flat on the table, and said, "How much?"

"It's been paid," he told me.

I ran to look for my *mechutan*, but he'd already taken his family home. I felt very uncomfortable.

When I got home, I took out both envelopes and opened the thin envelope first, the one with my name on it.

In it were invoices from the band, the photographer, the wedding hall, and the designer (whom I'd forgotten about completely). In addition, there was a small note: "We were waiting for the right time to give you some small gifts."

Exactly one year later, in *parashas Vayeishev*, I received a letter from the son. This is what he wrote: "Because of my commitment, we bought tefillin, and I put them on daily. But I feel a little bad because during the year, there were seven days where I missed and didn't put them on."

Then I discovered another note inside the envelope: "It's me, his father. My son makes sure to put on tefillin, but he feels really bad about the seven days he missed. Mostly, he's ashamed that he broke his promise to you. I don't know if this counts, but since I didn't make any promises to you, I put on his tefillin ten times. That makes up for what he forgot, doesn't it? Does that balance things out?"

The letters from the father and son touched me to such an extent that I found myself crying uncontrollably again.

I decided to call the son right then and there to express my admiration for his keeping his promise. I also wanted to reassure him that Hashem certainly forgives him for the seven days he forgot to put on tefillin, because, after all, he grew up in a home very far from religion, and something like that could certainly happen.

I called him. At the beginning of the conversation we talked about this and that and then he said, "Rabbi, I'm really sorry for those days I forgot to put on tefillin. It was on Pesach. We went away to a hotel for the week, and I forgot to pack my tefillin. How can I make it up?"

I didn't know whether to laugh or cry.

"Hashem loves you," I told him. "You may not know this, but on Shabbos, holidays, and *chol hamoed*, we don't put on tefillin."

That's the story. And because you like to put the message right there on the table, let me say that I think the message here is about caring about other people. If I had stayed with my feeling of being uncomfortable at interfering in other people's affairs, and if I hadn't acted like Yosef Hatzaddik, asking a stranger, "Why do you look sad?" the boy might have lost his fingers, and I would have missed the great privilege of helping a boy like him put on tefillin his whole life.

Shabbat on Highway 6

A family finds itself stuck at a gas station on Highway 6 for Shabbat.

There's no food, no blankets, and no roof over their heads. It's just them…and Am Yisrael. Secular, rightwing, leftist, fans of rival soccer teams Hapoel Tel Aviv and Beitar Jerusalem.

This is a story that will turn your heart in all directions.

Five years ago, we moved from Nahariya, where I had served as a community rabbi, to Ma'alot-Tarshiha, which is about twelve miles east. My sister and her husband came to live there, too.

One week, my mother, who lives in Ashkelon, invited us for Shabbat. We're a big, warm family and love to visit our parents. What's more, that Shabbat I was celebrating my thirty-third birthday.

My sister asked to join us for the ride, but I had a Toyota that only sat five.

I told her I'd have a problem taking her, what with two kids plus suitcases.

But I wanted to do her a favor, so I made a few phone calls. In the end, I traded my new car for a friend's old Mazda MPV, a minivan that seats seven. Now there'd be room for my sister and her husband plus their suitcases.

It's a two-hour trip to Ashkelon. We leave four hours before Shabbat, thinking that's plenty of time.

Big mistake.

We're fine driving out of Ma'alot-Tarshiha, but when we reach Yokneam, the car breaks down.

I have zero mechanical skills. Same for my brother-in-law. We call a few garages. They all say, "Give us a couple of minutes," but none of them get back to me. Meanwhile, time is passing. Still, I'm not worried.

No mechanic shows. Time to look for a different solution.

I decide to flag down a passing car, though I've never in my life done such a thing.

A car stops for me. The driver says he's a mechanic. He agrees to have a look.

After a short check, he tells me, "You've got a problem with one of the plugs." He runs back to his car, gets what he needs, replaces my spark plug, and the car starts.

The whole thing takes about forty minutes, and then we continue our trip to Ashkelon.

We merge onto Highway 6, which is a fast road, especially on Fridays. Usually, when you get onto Highway 6, you know when you're getting off.

Not in our case.

        🎬   🎬   🎬

No sooner do I get onto Highway 6 than the car stalls again.

I turn the steering wheel so the car drifts over to the shoulder. My brother-and-law and I get out of the car and look under the hood. We have no idea what to do.

Suddenly, the telephone service center of Highway 6 calls.

"We see from the cameras that you pulled over to the side. We're sending you a service vehicle. Meanwhile, move away from there. It's a dangerous place to stand. Take the children out of the car and over to the railroad tracks. There have been incidents when cars crashed into cars parked on the shoulder. Be careful."

Ten minutes later, the Highway 6 service vehicle arrives. The mechanic checks and tells me, "A plug went."

"I just replaced one twenty minutes ago," I tell him.

"So another one must have burned out," he says.

The mechanic replaces another spark plug, and we rush back into the car, now hoping to get to Ashkelon fifteen minutes before Shabbat.

Ten minutes later, that hope is gone—the car stalls for the third time.

Another service vehicle drives up fifteen nerve-racking minutes later. This time, the mechanic fixes some loose cables. I tell him to follow me in his car because I have to get off this middle-of-nowhere place called Highway 6.

He drives behind us.

I realize we will not make it to Ashkelon before Shabbat, so we began to rethink our plans.

I start calling people. My sister finds a friend who is the daughter of Rabbi Shimon Gabai, *ztz"l*, of Netanya, and she tells us, "Come to us for Shabbat. It will be our pleasure."

As soon as I know we have a place nearby to spend Shabbat, I relax.

Little did I know our adventures were just beginning.

🎬   🎬   🎬

Forty minutes before Shabbat, half a mile before the Highway 6 gas station, the engine begins to sputter. We somehow manage to crawl into the gas station, and that's where the car makes up its mind to die for the fourth time that day.

Thirty minutes till Shabbat. The anxiety is eating me up.

I spot a "Yellow" shuttle bus, walk over to it, and say to the driver, "Drive me to Netanya."

He tells me, "I've got workers to drive in another hour."

"I'll give you a thousand shekels."

He refuses.

"Two thousand."

"Forget it," he tells me. "I'm not budging from this place even if you give me ten thousand dollars. I'm not losing my job over it."

That's when I suddenly see there are only eight more minutes left until sunset. I wasn't aware of how fast time is passing.

And suddenly it hits me. Me, my wife, our two little children, my brother-in-law and sister-in-law—we're all going to spend Shabbat here at the gas station on Highway 6!

After a moment's shock, I catch myself and realize, *If you don't get organized for Shabbat somehow, you'll be stuck here with nothing.*

Running into the gas station's convenience store, I pick up ten large rolls, two big bags of pretzels, and a few cans of tuna. I pay and leave the store.

I call my mother to let her know what's happening. I also disconnect the car battery so the lights won't go on when I open the doors.

And then…it's Shabbat.

At first, things around us continue as usual, *yerachem Hashem*. Highway 6 is like a regular weekday. But as it grows darker, people come over to us and say, "Hi. You're *chareidi*, aren't you? Isn't it Shabbat already?"

"It sure is. It's been Shabbat for over an hour."

"So, how come you're driving?"

"Actually, I'm not."

"Then, where are you going to be for Shabbat?"

"Right here at the gas station."

They don't believe me.

"*Neshamah*, I'll give you a lift," they offer.

And I say, "Don't you understand? It's Shabbat now. I can't travel."

"Don't worry about it. We respect Shabbat, too. We even put the *chamin* on the hotplate. But you can't stay here. You've got young children."

And I explain to them, "There is only one justification for desecrating Shabbat: *pikuach nefesh*. Do you see any *pikuach nefesh* here?"

People find it hard to leave the gas station. A crowd forms. Everyone discusses what to do. One even wants to call the police, but other people say to him, "What for? Did he commit a crime? Leave him alone."

I go over to them and say, "Want to help me?"

Everyone says, "Sure, sure. Whatever you want. I'm willing to bring you back up north."

"Not north," I say. "More in the direction of Jerusalem. Just join me for a minyan for Arvit. That will really make me happy."

"Sure, we'll join," they say.

One of them, a distinguished-looking Ashkenazi, tells me, "I have never prayed in my life, but I must admit I admire you for sticking to your principles. I'll join your prayer." (He's the one who wanted to call the police.)

🎬   🎬   🎬

And so in the middle of nowhere, at a gas station on Highway 6, I say, "*Lechu neranana*," and start to sing. Half the people there know the melodies and join in. The rest try. I start to see what Am Yisrael could look like without *machloket*. In times of trouble, everyone joins with you. It really touches me.

At "*Lecha Dodi*," everyone knows the tune and joins in. And when I get to "*Bo'ee kallah Shabbat Malkata*," I start crying uncontrollably. That crying expresses a lot. It contains the guilt I feel for being responsible for the situation—how did I come to this, that my family is out here exposed to the elements for a whole Shabbat?—and also, an understanding that the *Borei Olam* brought me here and He surely knows why.

We pray Arvit, say, "Shabbat Shalom," and then on a stone table outside, we hold our *seudat Shabbat*.

Yes, *seudat Shabbat*. Two big rolls, tuna from a can, pretzels, and...lots of *chilbe*.

Huh? *Chilbe*? My father, may he live and be well, likes my *chilbe*, so we prepared a good supply to bring him. Now we had plenty of it.

I invite people to join, and some of them sit around us. I make Kiddush on Coca-Cola, break a roll, and give everyone a small piece with tuna.

"Look—we've got fish," I announce to my family, and we begin to sing the first *mizmor*.

Slowly, other people, young and old, join in. Everyone who comes to the gas station has a suggestion.

"*Achi*, you've gotta do something. I've got an Arab friend who will take you."

"Have Shabbat at my house. It's only ten minutes away."

Stuff like that.

After a few songs, it's time for the second course.

"Now for the soup," I announce and pull out the *chilbe*.

Everyone at the gas station gets a taste of the *chilbe*. Some say it's the best soup they've ever had. The kids are less excited. They take a spoonful, make a face, and go back to the tuna and pretzels.

Then I announce, "*Dvar Torah*."

It's a scene beyond belief. Some twenty or thirty people are standing or sitting around us, and I'm giving a Torah talk. I tell them I feel very emotional and don't know what to say and what not to say. I just know that I'm in a very big *nisayon*, and I'm excited to be there. I'm thrilled to be able to make a *kiddush Hashem*, and I promise them it will be the happiest Shabbat our family's ever had.

I see everyone's touched. They're as emotional as I am. They find it hard to leave.

When they do leave, they again tell me how worried they are. "What's going to happen overnight? Maybe we should bring you food and blankets."

I beg them not to. "Don't you dare," I say. "It will upset me a lot, and we won't even be able to use what you bring, so it's not worth it for you. Respect me and don't bring anything. Don't desecrate Shabbat for me."

They understand my position. Some ask, "Give us your name and phone number. We have to find out on Saturday night how you spent Shabbat."

I give them my name but refuse to tell them the phone number. I'm afraid they'll write it down. "Call information after Shabbat is over to get my number and give me a call."

⧆ ⧆ ⧆

The singing ends, night falls, and there we are, facing a challenge I hadn't given any thought to.

Without the sun, it's cold. Freezing.

It's the beginning of winter. I don't wish such a situation on my worst enemy. Open space. Strong winds. A cold that penetrates the bones.

I say to my wife, "You and my sister and the two children will sleep in the car. Cover yourselves with clothes from the suitcases and our suits. My brother-in-law and I will sleep on one of the benches."

All this time, people are milling around like it isn't even Shabbat. They come, fill up their tanks, and walk over to the *chareidi* family that's stuck. Everyone asks, "How did it happen?" and offers suggestions: "Let me drive you/bring you/call an ambulance." They all get the fact that I don't intend to move from this gas station no matter what. Which makes it hard for them to leave.

Hundreds of Jews—the not-yet-religious, the clueless—all, without exception, are kind and respectful. They try to help, but then realize I'm staying put and what will be will be.

⧆ ⧆ ⧆

At eleven-thirty, I lie down on the bench to try to sleep.

My brother-in-law and I are freezing. We have no idea it's dangerous, that you can die from something like this. It's called hypothermia. I'm after lap-band surgery. I lost one hundred thirty pounds, which makes me feel even colder.

I bite my lips until they bleed, but I don't realize I'm in danger.

At midnight, I wake up. I hear voices around me. I'm shaking and feel very weak.

I didn't wake up by myself.

Turns out, a few buses carrying fans of rival soccer teams heading home after a game up north were driving down Highway 6 when they saw us there on the bench.

They gather around us and see the state I'm in. One of them says, "Let's cover him, so he doesn't freeze to death on us."

What happens next? One after the other, they remove their team scarves—reds and yellows—and place them on top of me and Gabi.

Dozens of scarves are covering us when I wake up. I pull this improvised blanket tighter around me, see people standing there watching, and open my eyes wide.

"Are you okay?" they ask.

Clutching the scarves, I ask, "Where did all these scarves come from all of a sudden?"

One of them crouches down next to the bench and tells me, "Look, *achi*, we're fans of two rival teams. Enemies. You live in a different world, but if you check it out, you'll understand. There is no chance we will ever cooperate with one another. During a game, they need policemen and security guards to keep us apart. But we heard what you people did here for Shabbat, and now look—there are scarves in all colors. But they're not just colors. They're our ID. Each color signifies a rival camp. But here, everyone threw in their scarf, and they united for you. We're here to warm you up. And if it's okay with you, we have another pile of scarves for the women and children in the car."

For the second time that Shabbat, I start to cry. I don't think I'll ever again in my life feel the depth of emotion I feel there— to see dozens of people who usually hate each other suddenly

joining together in honor of Shabbat and those who keep it. It is
an unimaginable moment.

🎬   🎬   🎬

Someone there identifies himself as a doctor. He says to me,
"I think you were on the brink of hypothermia. I suggest you do
something to warm your body, maybe jump and dance."

"Come dance with me," I suggest to the crowd, and I start
to sing, *"Mi shema'amin lo mefached."* Everyone knows it, and
they all begin to sing with me.

And so, in the dead of night, on Highway 6, hundreds of
people are standing in a circle and singing, *"Mi shema'amin lo
mefached, et ha'emunah l'abed, velanu yesh et Melech ha'olam,
v'Hu shomer otanu mikulam*—One who believes is not afraid
of losing *emunah*, and we have the King of the universe, and He
protects us from everyone."

My wife and my sister and the two children get out of the
car, wrapped in dozens of scarves, to look on in wonder. I think
at this point, they also realize that this Shabbat is not exactly
a nightmare, but something much bigger than they can even
imagine.

After dancing for a long time, I say goodbye to everyone
with hugs and kisses, and return to the bench, sweating all over,
with the scarves warming me and preserving the heat I gener-
ated by dancing.

🎬   🎬   🎬

Morning arrives.

Again, the same flow of people who don't understand what
we're doing there, people who hear the story and realize I won't
accept any offers of "just let me give you a lift," who join the
minyan so they can at least fulfill one request of mine, and I and

my brother-in-law are praying with all the traditional melodies. And since it's also the Shabbat of my birthday, I recite from memory the entire *parashah* and *haftarah*.

Then comes the morning meal of fish (tuna), soup (*chilbe*), and lots of pretzels. And of course, Shabbat songs. Everything is more comfortable. The weather is pleasant. I make my children a *Tehillim* group, just like they're used to, and then an Avot U'banim program, just like they're used to. We even invented a game to replace their usual Shabbat afternoon time at the playground.

Motza'ei Shabbat arrives, and with it, a massive amount of calls.

Dozens of people who'd seen us call to ask what's happening and how we survived. Most say they're going to keep Shabbat fully or partially. I realize that something big happened here.

The Gabai family arrives with several cars to take us to their home. And wonder of wonders, our car springs to life. Which just proves to me that everything is planned down to the smallest detail by the *Borei Olam*.

We arrive in Netanya, take showers, and I'm privileged to *tovel* in Rav Gabai's mikvah. Then we return home.

End of story?

Nope. The beginning.

To this day, I am in contact with dozens of people who met me on that highway. All of them were strengthened in their Shabbat observance, with ten now fully keeping Shabbat. There are dozens of sub-stories from this strong connection created by a seemingly coincidental encounter at that gas station. It's truly unbelievable the ripple effect that Shabbat still has even now, five years later.

By the way, most of them call me, "Moshe Naaman, the Rabbi of Highway 6." I don't think the administration of Highway 6 objects to the title, probably because they don't have to pay a cent for it.

After this happened, I found myself wondering why I was privileged to have such an experience—to make such a *kiddush Hashem*, to celebrate such an elevating Shabbat that touched so many people, including, of course, myself and my family.

No sooner did the question enter my mind than the answer came as well.

My teacher was Rabbi Moshe Levy, *ztvk"l*. He was a Rav of Kisse Rahamim yeshivah, who died young after struggling with cancer for many years. Maran Harav Ovadia Yosef, *ztvk"l*, said of him during the shivah, "My replacement died."

As his student, I was privileged to publish in his memory: *HaIsh Moshe, Beit Toratecha*, and others.

But the highlight was one book on the halachot of Shabbat for Eidot Hamizrach, titled *Menuchat Ahavah*.

My effort into bringing out that *sefer* gave me the privilege of experiencing a Shabbat with *amecha Yisrael,* who went above and beyond and who forgot all the disputes between them for the sake of Shabbat and those who keep it.

It was truly a Shabbat of total *menuchat ahavah.*

Turnstile

A Jew on the brink of bankruptcy travels to America, hoping to find an investor to rescue him.

But someone who gets into trouble once can't seem to avoid it.

Of all the hundreds of millions of people in America, he finds himself arguing with...one of the few people who can help him.

Then he discovers that life is like a turnstile.

I got married about thirty years ago and joined a local *kollel*. Neither my parents nor my wife's are people of means. Far from it. So, unlike most of our friends, we didn't buy an apartment when we started out. We scraped by. I had to cover rent and living expenses from the *kollel* stipend and my wife's salary as a substitute teacher, which wasn't much.

I was constantly trying to think up ways to bring in more money, both to live on and to buy an apartment. Because my wife was only a substitute teacher, she had no regular paycheck and no benefits. As things stood, we'd never be able to afford our own home.

One day, I passed by a building and saw a sign advertising an apartment for sale for eighty thousand dollars. Thirty years ago, that was the price of a two-bedroom apartment. I decided to take a look. It turned out to be a three-bedroom apartment, but it was so run-down the owners knew they couldn't ask for more.

I realized things weren't as bad as they looked. Nothing a little plaster and paint job couldn't fix. Maybe new bathroom fixtures, too. The kitchen was a disaster, but if I replaced the cabinet doors and faucets, it could look okay.

When I got to *kollel*, I told everyone I just might have a good deal. I told them the plan: I'd buy the apartment for eighty thousand, put in ten thousand dollars' worth of renovations, and flip it for one hundred and twenty, which was the going price of a three-bedroom apartment in good condition.

Within a week, twenty-five members of the *kollel* were ready to partner with me. Each put in three thousand two hundred dollars, and I bought the place for seventy-six thousand (I got the sellers down on price). Together with the lawyer's fees, it came to eighty thousand.

Within a month, I'd brought the apartment up to a level even its former owners wouldn't have recognized. I quickly put it up for sale and, within days, sold it for one hundred and twenty-five thousand dollars, for a profit of thirty-five thousand dollars after expenses.

Every investor got his money back plus profit, and everyone was happy.

Not long after, I found another apartment. This one was going for fifty-seven thousand dollars. It took me exactly two days to raise the money and another two months to buy, renovate, and then sell it for one hundred and five thousand.

People heard about what I was doing, and *avreichim* began asking me to invest their money. And they wanted to invest larger amounts, too. People were putting in ten, twenty thousand dollars. That meant I could take on fewer investors and buy more pieces of property.

You wrote about this once, but I want to emphasize that *avreichim* are some of the sharpest guys around. They're quick on the uptake no matter what the subject. And their team spirit can't be beaten. Friendships are solid, and there's a lot of mutual trust. They're the best human material out there. They're willing to loan each other money, and they have no problem forming a group to invest.

I'd buy four apartments at a time and flip them for a nice profit. In just eighteen months, I'd made enough to buy my own apartment.

Remember, I was learning in *kollel* full-time. I sat and learned the whole day. When did I dabble in real estate? Between *sedarim* and at night.

I made sure to hire only top-rated professionals, workers who knew their job, but with an eye on value for the money. The calculations came easily to me. In no time at all, I could size up a property and estimate how much renovations would cost. I was a simple *kollel* guy who sat and learned, yet I was also a building contractor, real estate investor, and money manager.

Two years after I began, a great opportunity came my way. It was a five-story building with twenty apartments. The place was old, but it was a bargain. According to my calculations, after deducting purchase costs and renovations, I'd be making a 200-percent profit on my investment.

The initial investment was half a million dollars, and I raised the money in two hours.

I bought the building and started renovating it while trying to bring in more investors.

That's where I ran into trouble, big trouble, for the first time since I'd begun.

Two people who owned apartments in the building found a way to stop construction. They were trying to squeeze more money out of me by filing complaints at city hall. At the same time, an anonymous tip was made to the municipality, suggesting illegal construction had taken place in the building many years before I purchased it. Each day brought with it more and more people demanding money and threatening that if I didn't give it to them, they'd tie me up in court for years to come.

My first thought was to raise more money. What stopped me was worry that I might be risking the new investors' money along with the money already invested with me. I didn't want to do that to my fellow *kollel* members.

I stopped work on the project, which meant I was stuck with an investment of seven hundred fifty thousand dollars and no way to move forward.

I was sick with worry. The deal was a fantastic one, but all the problems I'd run into destroyed my self-confidence, and I couldn't bring myself to reach out to people who might help me. I even turned away *kollel* guys who wanted to invest. I was afraid this project was going to be a bottomless pit.

It was rough. I was just a simple *kollel* guy who now found himself facing enough debt to sink people a lot bigger than me.

I knew I hadn't committed any crime, but I'd be stiffing good people for money they'd worked hard for.

I consulted with an important Rav who advised me to travel abroad to raise funds so I could somehow finish the job and pay back the investors.

At the end of our meeting, the Rav gave me a very important piece of advice. "Before you go," the Rav said, "call all your investors to let them know you're making the trip, so they don't think you're fleeing the country. Otherwise, they'll be very worried and will put a lot of pressure on you to return their money right away."

I did exactly what he said. I told everyone I'd be traveling to the States to raise money. You could even say I sort of asked their permission to go. All, without exception, agreed.

I flew to the States. English was no problem for me since I'd lived in the States for part of my childhood.

I rented a basement apartment in Brooklyn and began making the rounds. I soon realized it would take me twenty years to raise the money that way. The quarters I was getting wouldn't cover any investment. I'd have to go back to Israel, and I was already counting the days.

On Friday, I went to the mikvah as usual. There's a turnstile at the entrance. You have to put in money or use a prepaid card to get in.

Just before I got to the turnstile, a *chassidishe bachur* came over to me and asked to double up with me in the turnstile.

This turnstile was like the one you use when you leave the Kosel. It's made for one person at a time, but two can squeeze in. The difference was that at the Kosel, it's free, but here, the *bachur* was trying to enter the mikvah without paying.

"It's wrong," I told him. "It's stealing."

"I have a prepaid card, but I left it at home," he told me. "Don't worry about it. It's fine. Everyone does it."

"Not me," I said. "So it's not everyone." As I spoke, I fed three quarters into the slot, pushed the turnstile bars, and walked through.

Once I was on the other side, I felt a pang of regret. First of all, maybe I'd hurt his feelings. Second, I said to myself, *Very nice that you're so careful about stealing, but what about the mitzvah of giving charity? There's a young bachur with no money who wants to go to the mikvah, and you won't let him?*

"I'll give you the money," I said to the *bachur.*

"But I have a prepaid card at home."

Ignoring his protests, I reached back through the turnstile and pushed three quarters into his hand. He had no choice but to drop them in the slot and walk through.

Right after him, an elderly man entered using a prepaid card. "Why didn't you let him go in with you?"

"Because it's stealing."

"But he told you he had a prepaid card at home."

"I know," I said. "But according to the mikvah's rules, a member must bring the card with him. The minute I let him go in without paying, I'm helping him steal."

"*Chaval*," the man said to me. "A *chassidishe bachur* tells you he has a prepaid card, and you don't believe him?"

When I left the mikvah, I again encountered the elderly man. He nodded in recognition. "You should have let him in."

"I let him in my own way," I said defensively. "I didn't leave him standing there outside. I paid out of my own pocket for him to come in."

"True," the man said. "You know what? I have an office in Manhattan. Come see me on Monday at nine."

Before I could ask him where the office was and what he wanted to talk to me about, he handed me his business card.

I stuck it in my pocket and went back to the basement apartment.

"I met someone who said he wants me to come to his office on Monday for a meeting," I told my roommate.

"Who?"

I showed him the business card. He looked like he was going faint.

"Are you serious? Do you know who this is?"

"No."

"This guy is the richest Jew in New York!" he exclaimed. "And most likely one of the wealthiest men in all America. He's Satmar's biggest donor. It takes *months* to get an appointment to see him. He distributes charity only through his foundation, never in person. This is a miracle!"

"I'm not so sure about that." I told him about the argument we'd had in the mikvah.

"Oh no." He shook his head in frustration. "Why did you have to argue with him? Couldn't you just say, 'you're right, and I was wrong'?"

"First of all, I didn't know who he was. But even if I had known, I still would have tried to explain my way of thinking to him."

He sighed. "I hope it doesn't come up again in your meeting with him."

"Me, too," I admitted.

We were both wrong.

I arrived at the office on Monday.

But it wasn't an office. It was more like a palace. It took up an entire floor of a Manhattan skyscraper. Upon entering, I was escorted by staff and secretaries through a world of luxury the likes of which I'd never seen.

I entered the boss's spacious room and was surprised to see two other people there as well, both younger.

"I want to tell you what happened to this Yid on Friday," he said to the other two, even before I sat down. "I'll tell you the story, and you'll judge between us."

He told them the story, gave his opinion, and then asked me to speak my mind.

At the time, we'd just exchanged opinions, but now we argued. Don't ask me why. So what if he's rich? Was I going to lie because of it?

"Why not believe the *chassidishe bachur*?" he said. "Do you think he'd lie for seventy-five cents?"

"Because I have no right to believe him. The one who has to believe him is the owner of the mikvah."

"But everyone does it."

"Maybe yes and maybe no, but according to the halachah, I'm not allowed to act like an owner of a mikvah that's not mine."

"Good," he said to the other two people in the room. "Now you *pasken* for us what you think."

Naturally, they "*paskened*" like him. As if they had a choice. You don't go against a man worth a billion dollars, especially if you work for him.

Too bad I myself realized this too late.

"Tell me something," he said to me. "Why are you here?"

I decided to tell him the whole story, how a simple *kollel yungerman* started flipping apartments, how the business grew until the latest deal that brought with it the problems I was facing, which is why I'd made the trip.

They listened. I saw their surprise and admiration at how I'd gotten started and what I had accomplished. And when I got to the part about the crisis that brought me there, they didn't blink.

I ended by saying, "I'm here in America to find a solution to the difficulty I've run into."

I saw a silent communication flash between them.

"Now we're completely certain," the boss said. "The reason I asked you to come in is that I have a business proposal for you."

"Listen," the boss said to me, "whether or not you're right about entering the mikvah, it shows how honest you are. Then, by paying for the boy to go in, you proved you're not only honest but quick on your feet to find solutions and a mensch as well. We've been looking for quite a while for a sharp, honest man of character to run our business in Eretz Yisrael, and we've decided to offer you the job. Just now, when you told us how you've carried out projects like those you described, we were convinced we've found the right person."

I felt the room spin around me. I searched their faces for signs they were joking but didn't find any.

"What business is it?" I asked.

"We have both real estate and charity dealings. We want someone we can trust to run them there. Exactly the kind of person who doesn't rely on himself when it comes to honesty and money. Someone who won't be 'lenient' at our expense or generous at his own expense but will manage things for our benefit and in our best interests without involving his own personal interests. The same way you handled matters there in the mikvah."

One of the others spoke up. "Regarding the building project that ran into a few snags—whether or not you work for us, we'll give you the missing funds so you can complete it."

The younger-looking one pulled out a contract.

"These are the conditions," he said. "Just sign here, and as far as we're concerned, you can go back right now and start running our businesses."

I glanced through the contract and looked up. "I know you don't expect me to sign on the spot. I'll have to take this with me and go over it. I also want to consult with others. Okay with you?"

They exchanged looks I didn't know how to interpret.

"Actually," the older of the two said, "we did think you'd sign it right now. That's what most people would do. But we're coming to realize that you're not like most people. Take the contract and let us know when you're ready to sign it."

I went back to the basement apartment, excited by the meeting I'd just had.

I sat down and started reading the contract.

My roommate couldn't get over the amazing *hashgachah* and kept talking about it until I suddenly interrupted him.

"I have a problem with two points."

"You're kidding, right?"

"No, I'm serious. They've got a section here stating that all their decisions are not open to review by anyone, and another paragraph that says they can add, subtract, or revise clauses in the contract as needed. I can't sign something like this."

"Are you for real?! Look what they're offering you. Look at the salary!" He pointed to the relevant paragraph in the contract. "Look at the benefits! Grab it!"

I sat there, not saying a thing.

The next day I went back to their office and sat down with the three of them again.

"The contract is fine, and I have nothing to say about the salary, but there are two clauses I can't sign."

"Which ones?" they wanted to know.

I told them.

"Don't worry about it," they said dismissively. "We need to cover ourselves, that's all. We can't have any pressure from rabbis, and at times, in certain situations, a clause may need to be amended. What's the problem?"

"I consider myself a serious *ben Torah,* and I'm sure you don't want to sign a contract with someone who isn't. You can put in a clause that gives you the right to fire me if you don't like my work, and that will cover everything. But I'll never sign a contract with a clause that diminishes the power of a halachic ruling by a Rav. It's not happening. As for adding and subtracting clauses, are you kidding? Would you want to hire someone who signed a clause like that?"

They laughed out loud, and then the big boss said, "You beat us. We'll take out those paragraphs, and you know what? We won't add the section you suggested about your dismissal. Satisfied?"

"Very much so," I said. "I really apologize for my chutzpah. When will the revised contract be ready? When should I come back?"

"It's ready right now," the youngest of them said as he casually pulled out another contract and put it on the desk in front of me.

I thought he was kidding. I looked over the contract and

was surprised to see it was identical to the first minus the two problematic clauses.

"Wait a minute," I said. "What's going on here? How did you know?"

"We were testing you," the boss said, and the three of them chuckled. "We wanted to see if you were serious. You got our approval."

For some reason, they found it funny.

"But—what about the mikvah?"

"Of course you were right," one said. "Do you think we support going into the mikvah without paying? That was your first test."

They cracked up.

"And the *chassidishe bachur?*"

They stopped laughing.

"No," the boss said. "He was real. That wasn't from us. You can thank Hashem for that one. I went to the mikvah like I do every Friday, saw what I saw, and said to myself, That's the kind of man we want working for us. You can thank Hashem. He and only He brought this test straight to you, without any go-betweens. He and no other."

That's the story. I flew back home with a substantial loan to complete the project and managed to pull everything together. Actual expenses turned out to be far beyond projected costs, but the project still made a big profit. The initial investors (my fellow *kollel* members), as well as the later investors (my new bosses in the States), did very well for themselves. I didn't do too badly, either, gaining a decent amount of cash plus two apartments in the building.

Since then, I've been managing the charity fund and the real estate business of the man who hired me. He's since retired, so I'm now working for his two sons—the ones I met in his office.

Some story, huh? The *hashgachah* of it all still leaves me in awe.

A Yerushalmi Miracle

The Yerushalmi's son is back with a story.

A young couple lives in poverty in a tiny apartment in the Old City.

As if that's not hard enough, a fire breaks out and makes their place uninhabitable.

Can anything get them out of this mess?

Apparently, even when you feel like you're up against the wall, you're in for a surprise when you discover what's behind it all.

This is the son of the Yerushalmi writing to you, the one who tries to follow in his father's footsteps, which occasionally includes sending you nice stories about Yerushalayim.

I have an incredible story to tell you about the Jewish Quarter in the Old City. But before I begin, I need to give you and your readers some background so you'll get the point of the miracle.

In 1948, when the State of Israel was founded, war broke out. The Jewish Quarter was captured by the Jordanians, and most of the synagogues and houses were bombed. Forty-nine people were killed, and the rest were miraculously saved and allowed to escape.

Nineteen years later, in 1967, another war took place. This time, the Western Wall and the Jewish Quarter were captured by Israel, which started to rebuild everything there.

Don't ask me why, but apparently, a higher-up decided he didn't want any *chareidim* in the Jewish Quarter, so they instituted all kinds of laws that allowed only the secular and national-religious to buy property there. Seriously. You can check it out, and you'll see that this is the absolute truth.

📣   📣   📣

Before I tell you about the Jewish Quarter, I want to tell you a little bit about Rabbi Yitzchak Shlomo Zilberman, *ztz"l*. If you've heard of the Zilberman method of *chinuch*, well, it's named after him.

My father told me that Rabbi Zilberman came from a Yekke family that moved to London as soon as the Nazis, *ym"sh*, came to power. In 1939, two years before I was born, he immigrated to Eretz Yisrael alone and studied at Yeshivas Kol Torah. He then learned under Rav Eliezer Yehuda Finkel, *ztz"l*, and was part of the original group of students to establish the Mir.

At that time, Sheindel, the daughter of Rav Yom Tov Zlotnik of Yerushalayim, was suggested to him. Don't ask. At first, Rabbi Zilberman's family objected. They even ran to the Chazon Ish to help them. But he said, "Marry her." And no one said anything, though Rabbi Zilberman did change his way of dressing from Litvishe to Yerushalmi.

Eighteen children, nine boys and nine girls, were born from this match.

Not many people know this, but Rabbi Zilberman was the

one who established the Kamenetz Talmud Torah and the Talmud Torah Hadar Zion. Because his teaching method was not accepted there, he established the Aderet Eliyahu cheder and yeshivah.

In 1988, his daughter, Rachel Weiss, was murdered with her three children on a bus traveling from Teveria to Yerushalayim. In 1991, he moved to the Jewish Quarter in the Old City of Yerushalayim.

And now, back to my story.

As I said before, a *chareidi* Jew was not allowed to buy property in the Jewish Quarter, but what logic can't accomplish, money can. In 1987, the Intifada began, and it became very dangerous to live in the Jewish Quarter. Most of the secular and half of the national-religious picked up their feet and fled. Though officially they weren't allowed to rent to *chareidim*, they turned a blind eye to that regulation, and the Jewish Quarter Development Company turned another blind eye, and so Rabbi Zilberman's people began renting houses in the Jewish Quarter. They didn't have the money to buy property, though the price then was the same as that of a regular apartment in the rest of the city. After all, where would these struggling Torah scholars get the money to buy even a regular apartment?

Don't ask what trouble they made for them. Let's just say it caused the Zilberman cheder to become very hyperactive. By that, I mean its location jumped from one place to another every day. As soon as the kids arrived at the cheder each morning, the police showed up to chase them away, ostensibly due to "a change in zoning laws." If you want to know the details, you can contact Rabbi Yitzchak Pindrus, who attended the Zilberman schools. He'll tell you all the difficulties they went through.

If at first the Zilberman people were viewed with suspicion—because Yerushalmis don't like anything new—once the "kids" grew up and became "goats," not a single Yerushalmi has a bad word to say about Rabbi Zilberman's group. When you see hundreds of *bachurim* and *avreichim* walking around wearing tefillin all day long, and they are *tzaddikim* and *yerei Shamayim*, refined and sensitive, you don't ask any questions, because you understand that the method is good, even if you didn't understand it.

As time went by, more and more *chareidim* rented houses in the Jewish Quarter from the secular owners who fled, until most of the Rova, as we call it, was filled with the students of Rabbi Zilberman.

I want to tell you about one house in particular that belonged to then Justice Minister Dan Meridor. He leased it to a Zilberman *kollel yungerman* for nineteen years. Maybe because he was the Minister of Justice, he allowed himself to break the law that prohibited renting an apartment to anyone who hadn't served in the army. Anyway, at a certain point, he offered the couple an option to buy the apartment from him.

Of course, the couple, who at the time had eight children, didn't have the money to cover the full cost of an apartment, so they had to take out a pretty big mortgage.

Plenty of people thought they were foolish. As I said, at that time, the houses in the Jewish Quarter were priced the same as houses elsewhere in the city, and between you and me, these homes had plenty of drawbacks. The buildings were old, the streets were narrow and hard to access, and if you found a way in, it was hard to get out. There were problems with sanitation, electricity, and plumbing. For the same price, you could buy an apartment in one of the newer parts of the city. "Why put your money into an old place?" people said to them. "Buy in the city and rent the place in the Old City.

But they bought it anyway, not dreaming what lay ahead of them.

About two months after they'd bought the apartment, a fire broke out, most likely from a defective plug, and their home burned down to the ground.

The news traveled fast in Yerushalayim, and when I say Yerushalayim, I mean Meah Shearim and, of course, the Jewish Quarter. The rest of the city wasn't interested in any fire or any old house in the Jewish Quarter.

A tragedy. An *avreich* with eight children who had just put everything he owned into a small two-and-a-half-room apartment, now needed to buy new clothes and household items plus renovate. It was a catastrophe.

Everyone was traumatized, except for...the Zilberman *avreich* and his wife.

In Yerushalayim, when there's a fire, everyone rushes to see from up close. Both because it's interesting, and also to show sympathy and offer words of consolation.

But everyone who talked to them came away stronger in their own *emunah*.

The couple told everyone how grateful they were to Hashem for saving them from the fire. They also said it was surely decreed on Rosh Hashanah for them to go through this experience, and they accepted the judgment with love. As for the future, does anyone ever know what the future will bring? If they'd been asked a week before what would be, would they have known their house would burn down? Now, too, they don't know what will happen after their house burned down. They'd also heard that a fire is a *segulah* for wealth, so it made them very happy.

Go argue with people like that. Everyone wanted to encourage them but came away themselves encouraged. Maybe I'm taking this statement out of context, and it really belongs with a story about consoling mourners. I promise to return it to its rightful place in due time.

But wait till you hear about the miracle hidden in this fire.

Their home insurance policy had a clause that covered fires, so all the renovations were paid for by the insurance company.

That's a miracle, too, but wait till you hear about the bigger miracle.

When the building contractor arrived at the burned-out apartment, the lady of the house told him that one of the walls made a big noise when you knocked on it. Because she had many young children, they banged into the walls now and then, whether on purpose or by accident, because the place was so crowded. But every time they banged into this particular wall, the sound made her jump. Was there anything he could do about it? Did he have any way of muffling the sound? Maybe some wallpaper or a layer of insulation?

"The wall is making noise, you say?" asked the contractor, who, by the way, was an Arab who knew the secrets of the Jewish Quarter as well as those of the Muslim Quarter.

"Yes, noise. Like a dull thud," she said.

"A dull thud, huh? Maybe you don't know walls, but walls don't make noise. Walls are silent. Believe me, lady, I've tried talking to a lot of walls, but it was like...like talking to the wall. Get it?"

"So, what could be making the noise?"

"Behind the wall is someone who wants to tell us something," said the contractor.

It sounds exactly as scary as it sounds.

Without another word, the contractor took a five-pound sledgehammer and began banging it against the wall hard enough to break it.

The couple thought he'd gone crazy, but before they could shout, "What are you doing?!" he broke a hole in the wall. It was too late for them to protest that the house was already in ruins, and there was no need for him to do further damage and make things worse. He widened the hole and soon found out who wanted to tell them a story...

And it was the most wonderful story they had ever heard.

Behind the wall was a small hall...the size of a four-room apartment.

The couple watched in amazement as the contractor continued to strike blow after blow at the wall. Soon he'd formed a makeshift doorway through which they stepped carefully into the greatest gift they'd ever received.

"So, you thought you had a two-and-a-half-room apartment?" the contractor said. "Well, now it's six and a half."

Dan Meridor couldn't have put it better.

The apartment was renovated (remember, at the insurance company's expense), and the couple moved out of a two-and-a-half-room apartment in terrible condition and into a six-and-a-half-room apartment in like-new condition.

As if that's not enough, in the 1990s, Americans suddenly became interested in the Jewish Quarter, and within a few years and to this very day, the value of a three-room apartment in the even worst condition is now three million dollars—one million dollars per room. A single-room basement goes for a million shekels, which brings in nice income for residents who go away for Shabbos or holidays to stay with their parents and rent out their apartment to tourists from Israel or abroad for a price that covers their monthly rent and allows them to live respectably.

Our couple is in even better shape because they own their apartment, and if they want to, they could sell it and pay for the weddings of all their children (all eleven of them).

So that's the story, Mr. Chaim Walder, and I hope you put it into your book because it has a historical dimension to it (I made some effort to find out about the history of the Jewish Quarter at the expense of my time). It has a short biography of Rabbi Zilberman and of the Zilberman method that is common in many places today. My father always said that when a G-d-fearing Jew goes with his truth without any calculations, Hashem helps him every step of the way. And most importantly, this is a thrilling story with a real mystery about the burned-down house with the talking wall, which turned out to be a great miracle full of *emunah* and *bitachon* in Hashem.

PS: I suggest you not call the story "The Burnt House with the Talking Wall," because then readers will run away thinking you've begun writing fiction, like you once tripped up with "Caveman." Just choose a title that will pull readers in. Once they're in, they won't be able to get out.

PPS: If they don't believe you even after all that, you can send them to Rav Ben Yashar, who gives tours of the Jewish Quarter. He will testify that the whole story is true.

Sincerely,
The son of the Yerushalmi

Peace Is Everything

A brother and sister aren't on speaking terms because of a brother-in-law's financial fiasco.

Maybe it sounds like the start of a good joke, but this story is far from humorous.

From being blood brothers, they become blood enemies—completely cutting all ties.

Is there a way to benefit from such a difficult, painful situation?

It turns out there is.

I want to share with you a very special event I attended recently.

It was the bris of the firstborn child of a woman in our family. But behind this bris, there's an extraordinary story with a message relevant to everyone.

This couple got married seventeen years ago, and if you noticed what I said about this being their firstborn, you've realized why I called it a very special event—a son after seventeen years of marriage. That in itself is an exciting story (though I believe there have been similar stories in the past), but the story here is much bigger.

The baby's parents, both from good families, were happily married for seventeen years. Theirs was a perfect match in all respects. Both came from prominent, well-to-do families. Both sets of in-laws were smart and very tactful people, the type that doesn't interfere and only wants to give. Relationships all around were wonderful, without jealousy or competition, just giving and sharing the joys.

The only cloud in the sky was the lack of children. After several years of marriage, it was worrisome, but everyone hoped for the best.

After seven years of marriage, one of the brothers-in-law made a few good deals and struck it rich, becoming a very wealthy man overnight. He quickly upgraded his standard of living by buying an eye-popping mansion and a late-model luxury car. Looking to make even more money, he became a serious investor in multimillion-dollar deals, generously inviting family, friends, and acquaintances to invest with him and reap the profits.

They'd never heard of Rav Mendel Shafran's rules, the first of which is: If a person suddenly rises up like a meteor, becomes a big philanthropist, starts driving the latest model luxury car and turns rich overnight—don't be impressed and don't rush to invest, just run away fast.

Lots of people invested their money with him and got good returns. The childless couple, the heroes of our story, had no money to invest. They watched from the sidelines and saw how others were earning a hefty return on their investment each month, and they were happy for them.

One day, the wealthy investor came to his sister and brother-in-law to ask a favor. Would they kindly act as guarantors for a large investment with great potential that he was about to undertake? Not for a minute did they wonder why such a wealthy individual needed the signatures of a couple that was broke. Knowing the extent of the brother-in-law's wealth, they signed on the dotted line without a moment's hesitation.

As did the rest of the family.

Like all stories about grandiose investments, this one, too, had a before...and an after.

One sunny day, the brother-in-law fled the country, leaving behind a debt of millions. People had invested heavily with him, but it all evaporated into thin air. At the bottom of the investment heap was our couple, the ones who hadn't had any money to invest in the first place. They found themselves saddled with a mindboggling mountain of debt because they'd signed as guarantors.

The couple was furious. Not only were they already struggling with one of life's most painful and difficult challenges; they now found themselves fighting in *beis din* and the courts against legal threats, among them the confiscation of all their possessions, a worry they'd never dreamed of. While their absconded family member was abroad, far from the creditors, they were faced with the insurmountable difficulties he'd created—unfair repayment for the favor they'd done him out of the goodness of their hearts.

When they realized no help would be coming from him, they declared they would never forgive him for the trouble he'd caused them—and they cut off all contact.

Several years passed. The couple still longing for children found themselves facing not only the emotional and financial stress of medical treatment but struggling to make large monthly payments to pay back the brother-in-law's creditors and wage difficult legal battles.

The anger and resentment they carried are too great for words. It was one thing to struggle with a difficulty that's Heaven-sent; it was another to face a hardship placed on them by a human being, especially a relative they'd treated kindly by doing him a favor. But what hurt them most was that he made no attempt to ask their forgiveness. Not many people can let such a thing go by.

Years went by, and they were still childless.

Over the years, various attempts at reconciliation were made by third parties. All were vehemently rejected.

Three years ago, out of the blue, an American family bought an apartment in this couple's building.

It was a very warm family blessed with many children. The two families soon formed a very close friendship.

The young couple babysat their neighbors' younger children when needed, and over time their home became a second home for them. The neighbors' children played, ate, and felt completely comfortable there. It was a win-win situation for both sides. One family got help carrying their load, and the other enjoyed the laughter and happiness of children, something they'd been missing for fourteen years. So despite the continuing financial difficulties and the crazy race to hug a child of their own, they found a little solace in their connection with the American family.

Two years passed, and then the eldest daughter of the

Americans got engaged to a boy from Lakewood. It was decided that the young couple would live in Lakewood, and the wedding would be held there, as well, since most of the relatives and friends of the two families lived in the States.

Given the close relationship, it was only natural for the Israeli couple to be invited to the wedding. When the American family had made aliyah, they'd left their home and furniture in place. They found it convenient to stay in their own home when they went back for *simchahs* or vacations. They invited their Israeli neighbors to stay at their home for three weeks: the week before the wedding, the week of *sheva berachos*, and the following week.

It may sound strange, but the relationship between the two families was so close and warm that neither side saw it as an imposition.

After a lot of indecision, mostly because the wife was afraid of flying, the couple decided to accept the invitation and use the opportunity to visit some of their own family members in the States.

The welcome mat was rolled out for them from the minute they stepped off the plane. The house was more like a five-star hotel than a private home, and they were treated like royalty until their departure.

Their hosts went above and beyond to give them a wonderful vacation. Despite their own intense schedule, their guests were treated to gourmet meals, sightseeing, and even surprises.

One day, the Israeli husband's mother called. She wanted to say that if they were already in America, maybe it was a sign they should think about reconciliation with his sister and brother-in-law, who had fled there.

"Ima, I don't think it's possible. We had a hard enough time emotionally coming here knowing they were here. But reconciliation? After all these difficult years?"

His mother didn't give up. She begged her son to grab the chance to meet with his sister and brother-in-law and make peace with them. She said the family conflict was breaking her heart far more than the debts she and her husband (the father-in-law of the bankrupt son-in-law) had incurred (yes, they too had gotten burned). She made it clear that if peace were made, it would give her a lot of *nachas*, which would certainly give them great *zechuyos*.

His mother also talked to his wife, her daughter-in-law. The daughter-in-law explained that she and her husband couldn't even think about forgiving the people who had run off and left them to face such debts and lawsuits without even an apology.

The mother-in-law cried to her daughter-in-law and said to her, "You're right, my dear daughter-in-law. I know I'm asking both of you for a heroic act that doesn't come naturally. But maybe Hashem will respond likewise by going above and beyond nature and blessing you with a child."

The mother-in-law then told her daughter-in-law a story about a woman named Miriam Gabay who, after being childless for ten years, went to Rav Shlomo Zalman Auerbach and asked for a blessing for children. He said to her, "Do something for Hashem that you don't have to do, and Hashem will give you something He doesn't have to give you."

Immediately upon hearing this, the woman began volunteering in hospitals and was soon blessed with a son.

As she was telling the story, the mother-in-law felt a kind of Heavenly enlightenment, as if the Shechinah was speaking through her.

"Listen to me," she said firmly. "If the two of you overcome your feelings of being in the right and if you do something you don't have to do, like meeting with my daughter and my son-in-law to make peace with them, despite feeling that rightfully they should be the ones to come to you, and even though you are still paying for what they did to you, at this time next year you will be making a bris."

The woman heard these words and burst into heartbreaking sobs.

Her husband was very surprised. How had his mother, whom he knew to be a rational, reasonable person, promised something that wasn't in her control to give? After all, so many rabbis had given blessings and prayed over the years. He and his wife had tried every *segulah* there was. How could his mother make an outright promise?

Truthfully, for a while he'd wanted to do what his mother was now suggesting, but he felt a responsibility for his wife. But now that his wife was urging him to do as his mother asked, and knowing how important making peace was to his parents, he decided to go ahead with it.

Two days later, in coordination with the American family and his parents, and calling on superhuman strength they never knew they had, the childless couple met with the brother-in-law and his wife. The latter said they were sorry and asked to be forgiven. They said their shame had held them back from coming to ask forgiveness. The childless couple said they forgave them completely for all the grief and anguish they'd been through. Nothing would bring back those lost years of suffering and debt repayment, but the reconciliation did ease things, especially since it gave them hope of becoming parents at long last.

A week later, they returned to Israel and picked up where they'd left off, after a trip full of enjoyable experiences.

And exactly nine months after that trip, they were blessed with a son.

The bris took place two weeks ago. As you can imagine, emotions were running high.

At the bris, the father spoke.

He talked about *parashas Vayeira* and the *mesirus nefesh* of Avraham Avinu for the mitzvah of hospitality. The Gemara says that in the merit of having guests, like Avraham Avinu, who pushed himself far beyond what a person would naturally do when ill, weak, and in pain, and yet overcame it with extraordinary effort, the Jewish people merited to get out of Egypt and dwell in the desert for forty years, also not according to nature.

"A person would have to be blind not to see that Hashem's salvation came to us in a way that is beyond nature," the father of the newborn said.

"People have big families, and it seems obvious: you get married, you have children, and life continues. Until it comes to people like us that God puts to the test. It seems that in our case, HaKadosh Baruch Hu waited for something to be done for Him. Everything we did over the years was not enough, but when we gave in, and also kept the mitzvah of honoring parents, which is the most important thing, we immediately got our hearts' desire without having to wait even a single extra minute."

He concluded with the following words: "I'm sharing this story for one reason and one reason only. I don't like to talk about myself, and I didn't want to tell it at all, but my wife insisted. She said we have to let people know about the miracle. When people outside our family heard it, they, too, said I should share it with as big an audience as possible. If by hearing this, other people are encouraged to take steps toward peace that they weren't able to do until now, and if we've managed to reunite people and heal broken hearts, let that be our reward."

The Photographer

You've probably heard plenty of stories about lawsuits. People sue companies, municipalities, and individuals as well.

Some claims are justified, others less so.

And some are nothing more than an attempt to squeeze a few hundred thousand out of an unsuspecting victim.

Here's a word of warning: Think twice before suing a wedding photographer.

I'm a well-known wedding photographer. My guess is that most of your readers have seen me at work at one of the countless weddings or other *simchas* I've photographed. I employ a team of dozens of photographers who work for me, and *baruch Hashem* there's plenty of work for all of them.

To many people, our job might look like nothing more than walking in, pressing a button a thousand times, and leaving. But photography in general, and wedding photography in particular, is one of the most demanding jobs around.

You work ten to twelve hours straight, from four in the afternoon till two in the morning. You can't sit down for a minute or even stand in one place. You've got to keep on the move, running around to catch all the best shots, carrying a ladder and climbing up and down it dozens of times in one night.

You start taking pictures at the bride's house, move to the hall, and at the end of the wedding, many families will ask you to do a photoshoot in Jaffa or the Old City or wherever.

And at the wedding itself, you have to be all over the place all the time. You can't miss a thing: the family portraits before the wedding, the *kesubah*-writing ceremony, the groom in his *kittel* having ashes placed on his forehead, the procession to the *chuppah*, taking shots of the people who get *kibbudim* under the *chuppah*, running to take the photographs in the *cheder yichud*, racing back to the hall to catch every table from several angles. You also strain your muscles, because the camera, whether for still shots or videos, is not an easy object to carry. And you also use your vocal cords, calling out to people, your lighting man, the assistant photographer, and you are under constant pressure not to miss the couple's grand entrance into the hall after they leave the *cheder yichud*.

During the dances, the photographer is dancing nonstop right alongside everyone else. Others do a few rounds and then rest, but the photographer can't rest for a minute. He's running around with his ladder, looking for good angles and under constant pressure not to miss a good shot.

By the end of the wedding, he's exhausted, but that's when the real work begins: the family portraits. People have all the time in the world, and you have to be a combination playgroup *morah*/teacher/principal to gather everyone together, to wait for the elderly aunt, to ask Yomtov to look straight ahead, to crack corny jokes to make everyone laugh, and afterward, when it's very late, to make your fourth trip to the ruins of Jaffa.

Which means coming home at four or five in the morning, knowing you have a bris at noon and another wedding at night.

In between, you also have to argue, because every wedding has its "after the wedding," and people tend to forget the rules that say there's an extra charge if you go over eight hours. They were planning on a certain amount, and suddenly they're told it's more than they thought. They tend to blame it on a billing trick, and when they discover they signed for this clause, they get even angrier with you because now you're not only a cheat but a cheat who got them to sign on the dotted line of his crooked scheme.

Then there are the arguments about the number of photos and the quality of the albums. Take my word for it, if anyone wants to make inquiries about a family for *shidduch* purposes, he should contact the photographer at their previous wedding. He'll know exactly how the *mechutan* handles his money...and his anger.

But that's a piece of advice that won't work with me because I have a "photographer's code of ethics" that says you won't hear a single bad word from me about anyone, even if the man who hired me put me through seven levels of Gehinnom at the wedding.

Two years ago, a large manila envelope was delivered to our office, addressed to me. The return address was that of a major law firm.

I opened the envelope and saw in big black letters: "Intent to Sue." On reading it, I discovered that someone was suing me for a large amount of money for breaking his leg.

Since I'd never broken anyone's leg, I read the claim carefully. I discovered that he didn't blame me directly but claimed that a camera cable caused him to trip and fall, and it was only through a miracle that he broke only his leg and not his head (though at this point I wasn't sure which was worth more...).

The bottom line was that he was demanding I pay him several hundred thousand shekels for pain and suffering, medical expenses, property taxes, water, and electricity.

Like any photographer with my size business, I don't deal with claims I make or those against me (most claims are by clients who don't want to pay what they signed to but aren't willing to give up the photos). I forward the claim to our lawyer and forget about it.

Usually, the lawyer contacts the insurance company, and if the claim is for a small amount, such as a complaint about a lighting assistant who spilled wine on a garment, or a fall of one kind or the other, the insurance company takes care of it. They pay the damages, and we pay a participation fee.

But this time, it was a claim for a large sum, and the insurance company decided it wanted to investigate.

The lawyer got back to me with questions about the claim. I told him, "I don't know any story like that. It's happened that people fell—once someone even broke his hand. But the minute someone falls, the photographers know about it, and they rush to help him get up and check to see that everything is okay. An incident of someone breaking his leg wouldn't go without any response from us."

"Please look into it," he said. "The insurance company is demanding we do so."

I had no choice. I asked one of my assistants to look over all the photographic material, locate a fall, and see if it was due to a camera cable, overly enthusiastic dancing, or from such delicious food that oil spilled on the floor and caused the claimant to slip.

To understand how difficult this task is, ask yourself if, in all honesty, you've ever watched a wedding video from beginning to end. I know lots of people who haven't even seen their own, let alone someone else's. There's a limit to how long you can stare at dancing that goes on and on…and on. And the further removed a person is from the *chassan* and *kallah*, the less time he wants to spend watching.

Now, talk to a photographer's assistant who sees the same events every day, except that the faces change, and ask him to watch the whole wedding from start to finish, and not just the finished product, but the raw footage, which means six hours times two cameras. In short, it's a nightmare.

It took my assistant a week to get back to me and tell me, "Listen, there's no one falling at this wedding from the first picture of the bride to the last picture of the whole family."

That didn't help me much. The claimant could always say the photographer didn't catch it, or worse, that he did but decided to edit that scene out. We realized we had to find a way to prove that the person who was suing was filmed leaving the wedding on his own two feet.

I sent out feelers to find out about the man suing me. It took a few days, but finally I made contact with someone who knew him.

We showed him the wedding video and asked him to identify the man for us from among the hundreds of participants.

It didn't take more than five minutes before he pointed to one of the dancers and said, "That's him."

We thanked him, and I gave my assistant the task of again looking through the videos, this time for the dancing man, to try to find evidence that he left the wedding with both legs intact.

Now the work was much easier. All he had to do was recognize the man and look for him from the beginning to the end.

It didn't take him more than a couple of hours to get back to me.

"From what I can see," he told me, "the man is seen walking toward the exit at about eleven and doesn't appear at the wedding again."

We looked repeatedly, and each time, there was the man heading out the exit and disappearing from sight.

But that wasn't good enough for me.

I asked the hall owners for the security camera footage taken at the time of the man's departure. It took us two days to receive it, but within only a few minutes of viewing we saw a man striding confidently out of the hall. Another security camera documented him in the parking lot, getting into his car and driving away.

We passed on our findings to the insurance company and were sure that was the end of it.

Were we wrong!

A month later, the lawyer called to say that the claimant insisted on suing me for damages to the tune of three hundred thousand shekels.

I was stunned. "Did you pass on the videos?"

"We passed them on to his lawyer, but they're set on going ahead with the lawsuit."

"And it doesn't seem strange to you?"

"It seems *very* strange," he said. "I've never encountered

anything like this. Usually, as soon as you catch the crook in his funny business, he evaporates into thin air and withdraws the claim. But this fellow is barreling ahead with his lawsuit fully confident he's going to win."

"What should we do?" I asked the lawyer.

"We'll go to court," he told me. "We'll expose his trickery and ask him to pay court costs."

Naturally, I agreed, though a red warning light flashed in my mind, like the kind that indicates a camera malfunction.

No one would be stupid enough to claim he fell when he knows he was photographed in good condition. The information had been provided to him to dissuade him from going to court, yet he wasn't backing down. Something strange was going on.

The day of the trial arrived. We were at the courthouse when his lawyers arrived. He didn't come. He didn't have to, either.

His claims were presented with documentation: hospital records showing evidence of a fall and a broken leg; a doctor's sick-leave permission letter; related medical expenses; loss of earnings; physiotherapy; treatment for emotional distress including depression. Anything he could stuff in there, he did.

Then it was my lawyer's turn to argue, and he argued as follows: "We do not doubt that the claimant fell and sustained a serious injury. However, the photographer (meaning me) did not cause this harm. The man did not trip over camera cables and apparently did not fall at all at the wedding. I request permission to show the court the security camera footage, which shows the claimant leaving the wedding and entering his car."

The court allowed three minutes of screening, and everyone saw the video about which experts stated that it was indeed a video from that day, taken by several cameras, with full-time synchronization.

The video came to an end. There was silence in the courtroom, and then the judge told the prosecuting attorney, "I don't understand why you wasted the court's time."

What could he say?

"In just one more minute," the prosecuting attorney told the court, "your honor will see that this video proves absolutely nothing about my client's claim."

A ripple of curiosity went through the group in the courtroom. Even the judge seemed intrigued.

"You'll have to do some magic to convince us that the tall, sturdy fellow in the video took a big fall that broke his leg yet was still able to walk gracefully to the parking lot and get into his car."

"You're right, your honor," the lawyer said. "Believe it or not, I'm about to do that magic. In just another minute, it will happen. I ask your honor for permission to make one very brief phone call."

The judge agreed.

The lawyer pulled out his cell phone, said one word, and hung up.

He'd exaggerated. It didn't take a minute. It took twenty seconds.

The door to the courtroom opened. A short, plump man hobbled into the courtroom on crutches, and the lawyer announced to the judge, "Your Honor, I present to you the claimant."

Jaws dropped. It was as clear as a thousand witnesses that this person was not the tall, sturdy fellow we'd all seen in the video.

A murmur filled the courtroom. It took a while for the judge to collect his thoughts.

"You probably did the right job," the judge said to my lawyer, "but not on the right person. I suggest we take a half-hour break during which both parties will leave the courtroom and try to settle the matter between you."

"Okay with you?" my lawyer asked me.

"No," I said. "I don't want to settle."

A hush descended on the courtroom.

The lawyer, the judge, and frankly, everyone who had eyes and ears, looked at me in astonishment.

"I understand that you are the photographer," the judge said. "Are you aware that you have not presented a legitimate line of defense against the accusations?"

"Can I say something?" I asked.

"I will let you speak," the judge said, "but I must warn you that you may say things that can be used against you since you are not a lawyer and don't know procedure. There is legal significance to what you say here."

"That's fine," I said calmly. "I am by no means a lawyer. I'm a photographer, and I wanted to tell you, your honor, and everyone here in this courtroom that crooks can sue all kinds of businesses and car owners and municipalities and private and public institutions, but suing a photographer is not advisable at all, as you will find out later."

Then I said: "We did painstaking work to find the man in the video and sync all the videos related to him. We were confident that as soon as we told the other side what we'd found, the claimant would pack up his lawsuit and leave. When he didn't, my lawyer understood it one way, and I another. He understood that we were going to crush him—but I realized that somebody was out to trick us.

"I considered the plaintiff's overconfidence and realized there must be something he knew that I didn't. Then I sat and thought about where I might have gone wrong. Just like searching for missing keys, I went back over all my steps in reverse. I rechecked all the videos, and then I got back to the starting point: the networking I did to identify the man who'd fallen.

"The person who gave me the information was a member of the family. He's the one who looked at the videos and identified the man. It occurred to me that he might be less innocent than I'd thought. Maybe he'd been sent by someone to mislead me.

"I made further inquiries, and in no time at all, I had the real name of the man who'd been photographed. I found out that he was not a relative, but a neighbor of one of the parents.

"Now I understood the claimant's supreme confidence. He'd sent me a brother-in-law to mislead me. It took me one more day to find out who the real plaintiff was, as well as that his true body size was totally different from the man we were told was the plaintiff. I even got a photo of him with no trouble whatsoever. You know, I'm a photographer. It's not hard for a photographer to get photos.

"And then I looked at the wedding videos again and made another discovery: He wasn't even at the wedding, though he does know the family. I now had a partial advantage over him because I was on to the deception. But I knew that as long as I didn't prove without any doubt that he didn't fall at the wedding, nothing would help me. He could always claim the camera missed it, or we'd edited it out of the videos.

"I began by assuming that the man had probably fallen sometime before the wedding, but had delayed going to the hospital until the time of the wedding to make some money out of it. With that in mind, I approached all the shopkeepers in the area where he lived. Fortunately, he lives in an area with many stores, and I asked them all for their security videos.

"We watched videos from all the surveillance cameras, the ones taken when the wedding took place, and within two days we'd discovered the whole truth. I ask the court's permission to show the video we put together."

The judge allowed it despite the prosecuting lawyer's protests. The video began playing, including my voiceover narration of the visual evidence.

"Here the claimant is seen leaving his house at nine supported by two men" (probably his children) "and being helped into a car that then drove away.

"We were able to get a number of security videos along the route they took, but they're not important. Here you see the car entering the hospital parking lot. We got this video from the kiosk opposite the hospital entrance. Unfortunately, the hospital did not give us permission to view their security videos, but we can prove the time he arrived home, which was four in the afternoon. From that time on, he did not leave his house, which means that his fall probably occurred at home or in the stairwell. If the prosecution claims that the claimant drove from the wedding to his home and then to the hospital, we will bring the security footage and prove what time he arrived home. Does your honor now see why I didn't agree to settle?"

You could have heard a pin drop.

The judge seemed fascinated. He looked at the prosecuting attorney, who looked even grayer than the security videos.

"I think your client was trying to deceive the last man in the world to try this kind of a scam on," the judge told him. "Do you want to reach an agreement on the legal fees you will have to pay the defendant, or would you like me to determine the amount?"

The lawyers left the courtroom and returned five minutes later.

"We have reached an agreement on the payment of the legal fees."

The judge gave his stamp of approval and added harsh words about the plaintiff's attempted fraud. He left an opening for my counterclaim for the time I spent to prove his fraud.

On the way out of court, the lawyer asked me, "Tell me something. If you knew ahead of time what was going to happen here, why did you put on the whole show? Why didn't you tell me about your discovery so I could at least try to get him to drop the lawsuit?"

"I thought about it," I said apologetically, "but I knew you'd go according to due legal process. I knew, though, that I was dealing with a sophisticated person and that if I gave him time, he'd find some sneaky way to renew his claim. He'd try to say he was at the wedding and then went back home and—"

"But you disproved that," the lawyer said. "You had security videos that saw him coming home at four."

"You're a lawyer," I told him, "and a lawyer should pay close attention to every word. I didn't say I *had* those security videos. What I said was, and I quote, 'If the prosecution claims that the claimant drove from the wedding to his home and then to the hospital, we will bring the security footage and prove what time he arrived home.' I didn't say I *had* those videos because I don't. I knew he knew he wasn't at the wedding because he didn't appear in the photos, but I couldn't use it because he'd say I destroyed the photos. That's why I pulled this trick, which made him, like you, think I had such security videos."

The lawyer raised his hands and said, "I don't know why you chose to be a photographer. You should have been a lawyer or a detective. What I do know is that if anyone ever comes to me and asks me to sue a photographer, I'm going to think twice before taking the case."

That's the story, and it's the kind of story I think will interest you and your readers. The main takeaway is to remember that the greatest photographer of all sits in Heaven, where there's an eye that sees, an ear that hears, and all your deeds are written in a book.

The Blessing of the "Kohen Gadol"

A veteran teacher is offered an unexpected promotion.

She's about to accept when she discovers that her happiness will come at the expense of a woman still yearning for children after many years of marriage.

The teacher and her husband go to Chacham Shalom Cohen, shlita, and tell him the whole story.

This is a story about wisdom, good middos, emunat tzaddikim, and...the power of the blessing of the "kohen gadol."

This is the first time I'm going public with my story. Partly, it's because the story isn't mine alone to share, and I was hesitant to ask the other party involved for their permission to go public with it.

But a recent event propelled the story into the limelight again in a very dramatic way.

Actually, there are two stories here, both of them the "once in a lifetime" type.

As we know, every delay is for the best. Had I told you this story several years ago, it would have been only half a story. Now it's complete and even more powerful.

🎬 　 🎬 　 🎬

I got married twenty-five years ago. I joined a *kollel*, and my wife worked as a teacher. It looked like a good life, and it was.

Only one thing was missing in this perfect picture. And that one thing was the most important thing in the world.

Children.

For the first few years, we weren't overly concerned, but as time went on, we knew we had a problem. We began the journey that back then was known only to infertile couples and their families. Now, due to such stories being publicized, the general public is more knowledgeable as well.

Our journey, like that of most, was a hard, grueling, rock-strewn trek through uncharted territory. There's a destination, but no estimated arrival time—and in fact, no guarantee you'll get there at all.

We spent a lot of money on doctors and spared no effort medically or spiritually. We prayed at graves of tzaddikim, went wherever we could to get blessings, and tried too many *segulot* to mention.

Still, nothing happened.

At one point, I was able to get in to see Rav Ovadia Yosef, *ztz"l*. After the first visit, I went back to him from time to time for a blessing.

Rav Ovadia took our story to heart. He spent more time with me than the usual and showered me with generous blessings. He also gave me a few strong slaps on the cheek, given to those he favored as a sign of affection as well as evidence to his desire to encourage us and bless us.

One day, Rav Ovadia surprised me by saying, "Go to Chacham Shalom Cohen. He has a holy mouth that speaks only words of Torah. Words that leave his mouth are fulfilled. Tell him I'm asking him to bless you."

Those were his exact words.

He gave me a few loving slaps, and I left.

Today, everyone knows of Chacham Shalom Cohen, one of the *gedolei hador* and the head of the Moetzet Chachmei HaTorah. Back then, he was best known in the *chareidi* world for being the Rosh Yeshivah of Porat Yosef (a position he still holds), a man who shunned the limelight or any public position—a giant of a man whose whole world was Torah and only Torah.

I went to Rav Cohen's house in the Old City at a time when I knew he'd be home.

He was sitting in a corner near a bookshelf, learning. His concentration was so deep that my presence went unnoticed until a family member managed to get his attention.

I told Rav Cohen why I'd come.

"Tell me your name and your wife's," he said. "We'll pray, and Hashem will help."

He handed me a small piece of paper on which I wrote our names. I watched as he placed it underneath his Gemara, where it joined the other pieces of paper there.

He shook my hand and said, "May there be *besurot tovot* (good news)."

I left in turmoil. There was something powerful, fatherly, poignant—something about his very being and the purity I saw in his face moved me deeply. As Rav Ovadia said, "He has a holy mouth that speaks only words of Torah." You could see from him and his humble home that he had separated himself from This World. It moved me then, and I still get emotional when I think about the mutual admiration of these Torah giants despite—or perhaps because of—the differences between them.

When I got home and told my wife about the meeting, she had one question.

"Did he *promise* we'd have children?"

"No," I told her. "He didn't promise. He just said he'd pray."

✄   ✄   ✄

We continued our *hishtadlut*, following the advice of rabbis and doctors, but nothing changed.

I returned to Maran's house, and he blessed me again. Then he asked, "Did you go to Chacham Shalom?"

"Yes."

"And?"

"He gave me a blessing."

"Tell him that I'm asking him to promise you," Rav Ovadia said. "It's a holy mouth. Whatever comes out of his mouth happens."

I left Rav Ovadia and told one of the people close to him what he'd told me. He said, "Wait until Yom Kippur. Rent an apartment in the Old City and go pray with Chacham Shalom. Go to him on Yom Kippur and ask for a blessing. It's a holy day, and when the '*kohen gadol*' gives a blessing, it comes true."

Beginning that year, I prayed at Yeshivat Porat Yosef in the Old City every Yom Kippur. After the service, when everyone passed by the "*kohen gadol*," I would remove my tallit from my head so he could see who I was, and then I'd ask him for a blessing. He would bless me with special warmth (despite his serious demeanor on Yom Kippur). But a promise? I didn't have the courage to ask.

That's how it went, year after year, for fifteen years. Fifteen Yom Kippurs. And eighteen years of childlessness.

Our lives became gray and bitter. I don't want to go into detail, nor do I think I need to. Everyone knows that children make a family.

Over the years, we watched as our friends and siblings celebrated bar mitzvahs and those who had married only a few years before us even began marrying off children—while we remained just the two of us, alone with our pain, loneliness, anguish, and worry.

As if that wasn't enough, we suddenly ran into big trouble.

As I told you, my wife was a teacher. Eventually, she was made assistant principal.

The position of assistant principal confers a lot of authority—and an even greater measure of responsibility. The job gave her deep satisfaction and happiness.

Her principal was there for her in every way, guiding her and teaching her everything she needed to know to fulfill her duties to perfection. It was an open secret that my wife was being groomed to take over the principal's job when she retired.

Eventually, that day came, and my wife and I looked forward to receiving official notice of her appointment as principal.

For some strange reason, though, the notice never came.

The retiring principal was not involved in the process. The decision was up to the head of the large network of schools to which my wife's school belonged. The outgoing principal passed on her warmest recommendation, but beyond that, she had no authority or say in who would replace her.

One day at the beginning of Adar, my wife got a phone call. "Hello?"

"Uh…hello," she heard a woman say. "This is (she stated her name; my wife recognized her as a teacher a couple of years younger than she was). I'm calling for the assistant principal?"

"Speaking."

"So, it's like this. Yesterday they told me I've been given the job of principal at your school."

"*What?!*"

I was surprised to hear my wife cry out like that. She's a very soft-spoken person.

I walked over to where she was sitting with the phone and heard her say, "Who told you that?"

"The head of the network told me."

My wife put her hand over the phone to block the sound and whispered to me, "They made someone else principal."

It was a good thing she couldn't see herself. She was as white as chalk. I thought she'd faint or worse.

She switched to speakerphone.

"Why are you calling?" my wife asked, finding her voice at last after the initial shock.

"I'm calling because I can't take the job without your permission."

My wife was speechless.

"I don't understand," she said after a long pause. "Why do you need my permission? I'm not the one who decides. Did someone send you to get my consent?"

"No," the woman said. "And I know they'd be mad at me if they knew I was making this call."

"So why are you?"

"I'll tell you the truth," the teacher said. "They called me down to the main office, where they told me the news and had an informal ceremony. I went home happy as could be and told my husband about the surprising promotion.

"I told a few fellow teachers, who were very excited for me and wished me a lot of success. But then one of them, who's a substitute at your school, said, 'Wait a minute. I don't understand. Why did they skip over Batya?' (That's my wife's name.)

"'Who's Batya?' I asked her, and she told me you're the assistant principal, and everyone knew you were going to become the next principal. I hung up and started to check into the matter. I heard very good things about you, and then my husband suggested I call a certain person in the network's administration. I made the call and asked if you'd given your consent to me being appointed principal.

"'Why does that matter to you?' she asked me.

"'You should have told me there was someone waiting to step into the position,' I said. 'I wouldn't want something like this done to me.'

"The woman I was speaking with got angry," the teacher told my wife. "She said it's none of my business, that I'd been given an opportunity and I should take it and not get involved in how the administration makes its decisions.

"'And for your information,' she added, 'there are other candidates. If you don't want the job, someone else will take it!' and with that, she ended the call.

"I thought about it all night," the teacher said. "My husband and I decided I wouldn't take the position without first getting your permission."

"What if I don't give it?" my wife asked.

"Then I'll tell them sorry but no," the teacher said.

My wife was moved to tears.

"Where are you from?" she asked the teacher.

"Why are you asking?"

"Because I didn't think there was a place in the world with people like you."

"It's not me, it's my husband."

"It's both you and your husband, but mostly it's you," my wife said. "Let me think it over. I'll get back to you tomorrow."

We couldn't believe what we'd just experienced. And truthfully, we were somewhat confused. The realization that they'd deliberately denied my wife the promotion came as a blow that left us reeling. On the other hand...the phone call. The kindness. The sheer goodness of the offer, the likes of which we'd never before encountered. We felt like the forces of evil had met their match when they encountered these powerful forces of good.

And that gave us a very good feeling.

But we were facing a huge question. What should we tell her? Should we ask her to turn down the job offer? It wouldn't help anyway. Should we agree to her taking the position? How could we lend a hand to a process that was obviously unfair and tainted by other interests?

We decided to ask *daas Torah*. Naturally, I decided to bring the question to Chacham Shalom Cohen.

I went to his house in the Old City and told him the story. I covered all angles and then asked if we should agree or tell the teacher we don't agree.

I was surprised when Chacham Shalom ignored my question. He got very emotional after hearing the story. For the first time in my life, I saw him get excited. Usually, he was very focused on the issue at hand and anxious to return to his Gemara. Not now. I thought I saw tears in his eyes.

He asked me repeatedly to tell him the details of the story

and wanted to know what brought the teacher and her husband to act with such nobility.

"*Zeh maaseh gadol meod* (this is a very great deed)," he said. "If they come to me, I will give them a special blessing."

I burst out crying. The special interest shown by Chacham Cohen made me realize what a preciously rare event was taking place in my life.

"I will think the matter over and give you an answer tomorrow," the tzaddik said. "Call him as well to come to me," he added, referring to the husband of the teacher. "I want to talk to him."

We came the next day.

Chacham Shalom sat on his chair and welcomed the teacher's husband with special warmth and showered him with praise.

"I want you to know," the tzaddik said, "that you and your wife did a deed so elevated it reaches all the way to the *Kisei Hakavod*. It's a deed that shakes the worlds. HaKadosh Baruch Hu is very happy with you for what you did. Pray and ask Him for what you want most—it's a time of *ratzon!*"

The teacher's husband looked torn. You could see he wanted to say something but was too uncomfortable to do so. I told him I'd leave the room, but he said with sudden determination, "Don't leave. I want you to stay."

He then spoke to Chacham Shalom.

"*Kevod Harav*," he said, "the main consideration of my wife and I was not to cause pain to a woman who's been childless for eighteen years. I want to ask at this propitious time that in exchange for my wife's deed, the Rav bless this man and his wife and promise them a child soon. That will be our reward."

I couldn't believe what I was hearing. I burst out crying like never before. The teacher's husband had tears in his eyes, and Chacham Shalom hid his face. It was a unique moment in time like none other. What a special person! For him and his wife to do such a rare and noble deed! And then, when they had a chance to be rewarded for it, to choose to ask that a complete stranger get the reward instead!

Time stood still, and then Chacham Shalom removed his hand from his face, looked straight at me, and for the first time in my life, after so very many tries, finally, in just four words delivered the decree: "*B'siyatta diShmaya*—this year!"

Then he said to the man, "Your wife will tell them she doesn't want the job. I'll send someone to take care of the rest. You won't lose out."

Just before he left, the man said to Chacham Shalom with a smile in his voice, "*Kevod Harav*, I still haven't gotten my blessing. Please promise me that if I ever need a *yeshuah*, the Rav will pray for me."

Chacham Shalom Cohen gave him a loving smile. Before the man reached the door, he was already deeply immersed in his learning.

Outside, the man and I gave each other a strong hug, and I ran to tell my wife that we'd gotten an outright promise.

The teacher told the administrators of the school network that she wouldn't be taking the job. They reacted with fury and offered the position to others. But word of the teacher's rejection of the job offer spread like wildfire, and no one wanted the job—whether because of the truth or due to fear of public disapproval.

A month later, they called my wife to offer her the job.

And nine months later, we were holding our son. The promise of Chacham Shalom Cohen had been fulfilled.

It's now eighteen years later. We've been blessed with more

children, and have sent others to ask Chacham Shalom for his blessing.

I promised you two stories. That was the first. Here's the second.

Five years ago, the daughter of that wonderful teacher with such beautiful *middos* became ill with the dreaded disease. She was nineteen and just about to begin *shidduchim*.

Her parents turned over the world to get her the right help, but her condition steadily deteriorated.

One day, they came to us.

I knew right away why they'd come. As sad as we were about the reason for their visit, we felt grateful to be of assistance in any way we could to repay this wonderful couple for their kindness to us.

The teacher told us she'd been stuck career-wise ever since that incident. She hadn't gotten a single promotion. Every time an opportunity arose, she'd been told, "You already got your promotion." Even when she asked for extra hours or to teach a higher grade, things usually given as a matter of course, someone (and always the same someone) would drum her fingers on the armrest of her executive chair and say, "You were such a do-gooder, weren't you? So now accept the consequences. You already got your promotion."

One day, when she came to make a request, this same administrator asked her, "Tell me something. You know you're not going to get it, so why do you keep coming to ask only to get a negative answer again and again?"

Here's what the teacher said.

"I'll tell you why. True, I didn't get to be principal. But Hashem rewarded us in many other ways. I opened a nationwide educational project that brings in more money than even you earn. Plus, I'm still enjoying my role as a teacher. And do you know why it happened? Because Hashem saw what I gave up. As for your question about why I keep coming back to ask you when I know you'll just drum your fingers on your armrest and tell me with a smile that I've already gotten my promotion, it's like this: I come specifically to hear those very words. Because not only do I hear them, but Hashem does, too. And as soon as that happens, He immediately showers my family and me with the most amazing blessings. I don't really need the promotion. I need those words. It's just the opposite of what you thought."

And then she left.

"And now," the teacher told us, "we're in big trouble. We've never forgotten the promise from Chacham Shalom Cohen, and we want to ask him for it now. We want you to come with us to his house to reawaken those special moments."

Of course we said yes.

This took place two years ago, three years after their daughter's diagnosis, when her life was hanging by a thread.

We went to his house. It was Taanit Esther. He recognized us immediately and was pained to hear about their daughter's illness. We didn't need to remind him of anything. The whole story was as fresh in his mind as if it had taken place that same day.

The Rav asked them in detail about their daughter's illness and about the doctors and treatments and then gave his advice. We asked him to give a blessing and a promise, but he didn't seem to hear us. We learned later that he was then dealing with one of the most complex public issues to affect the Jewish people in recent years. As the leader of Sephardic Jewry at whose directions governments rose and fell, his was the final word.

A family member came over to us and said in an undertone,

"Come for the Purim *seudah*. Ask whatever you want. The Rav gives blessings."

We all came back for the Purim *seudah*. The Rav was surrounded by dozens of people along with his family, including dozens of grandchildren. We made our way through the crowd until we stood there before him. Now, at the Purim *seudah*, with everyone mellow from fine wine and fully aware that it was a day designated for miracles and salvation, the family of the sick girl found the courage to ask for her to be healed.

"*Harav!*" the father shouted. "I need a blessing!" He started to cry and couldn't stop. His tears flowed in an endless stream. "Does the Rav remember the blessing I didn't take a few years ago? Well, now I want it. *I need it.*" He was crying like a baby. His daughter's life hung in the balance, and nothing was going to stop him.

The "*kohen gadol*" took his hands in his own compassionately and smiled. It was the exact same smile he'd given him back then—and we knew the Rav remembered exactly what he'd said back then. He took a glass of wine full to the brim and handed it to the sobbing father.

"*L'chaim*," he said. "*L'chaim tovim u'leshalom.* Health, a full and speedy recovery to your daughter! Don't listen to what the doctors say. Be happy!"

We left, bursting with joy.

I couldn't wait to see what would happen.

In the coming months, the man's daughter underwent several treatments and an operation, and by the following Purim, we were able to give Chacham Shalom the good news that against all medical expectations, the girl had made a complete recovery, as he had blessed and decreed.

Why am I telling you all this right now?

Because a month ago, the girl got married. The *mesader kiddushin* was Chacham Shalom Cohen. My wife and I attended the wedding. We brought our eldest son, and I even served as a witness. Only a handful of people in attendance knew the unbelievable story behind that wedding.

Besides wanting to share with people everywhere the story's powerful message about giving—especially giving up what's precious to us for the sake of another—I want to express publicly my thanks to Chacham Shalom Cohen, *shlita*. May Hashem grant him many more years of life in good health. I'm a witness to the extent to which his blessings, the blessings of the "*kohen gadol*," are fulfilled. I was concerned that telling this story might add considerably to his burden, causing even more people to flock to him to get his blessings, but if others benefit, I can't hold that back from them. Besides, word has already spread about the power of his blessings. As Rav Ovadia Yosef said so many years ago, "Go to Chacham Shalom Cohen, Rosh Yeshivah of Porat Yosef. He has a holy mouth that speaks only words of Torah. Words that leave his mouth are fulfilled."

Endless Light

Employees of a company run by a well-known chareidi billionaire argue over whether their boss would betray his principles to avoid a million-dollar loss. It's all speculation...until such a test actually presents itself.

When it does, it's not just a million dollars on the line, but every single penny to his name.

I haven't told this story to anyone. Ever. Mostly because I'm afraid. Still, I knew it *should* be told because it's very unusual. Incredible, actually.

I live in one of the wealthiest communities in Israel. I work in international trading. In what area? I prefer not to say.

One year, I got into trouble, through no fault of my own, and nearly went bankrupt. It was a very tough time because where I live, if you don't have money, you don't exist. We had money for food and enough to keep a roof over our heads. I didn't fall *that* far. It's just that regular life in our area is very expensive. People here live in another world from ordinary mortals. If a birthday party for a three-year-old costs 150 shekels everywhere else in the country, here it can run to a 100,000 shekels. I'm not exaggerating, either. As for a bas mitzvah party, a wedding, clothes, and vacations, let's not go into it. Bottom line, you need a minimum of 300,000 shekels a month to keep up with the circle I'm in. And there are places where you need a million or more.

(Let me just say, in parentheses, that most people are jealous of wealthy people. It never occurs to them that the financial pressures faced by the rich are many times more than those of the average person. The wealthier a person becomes, the more frequently he encounters people wealthier than he is. A person can find himself spending on a watch enough to support your average Bnei Brak family for two years. For a watch! A watch he replaces a few months later. The ones who really live the good life are the *kollel* families who live within a budget and aren't looking to live a luxurious lifestyle. They're the ones who live without an overdraft and even manage to save up for their children's weddings. How do I know? Read on and you'll find out.)

From being where I was, I suddenly found myself having to watch expenses like electricity and the cars (yes, plural), and cutting back on travel and nonessential expenditures. Still, if nothing changed, within a few months, my wife and I would be forced to move.

Don't think it was because we'd have to sell our house. No, it wasn't that. It was because of the outrageously expensive lifestyle of our children's friends.

At this time, I was offered a job by someone younger than I. He was a very wealthy individual who also worked in international trade. But unlike me, the (former) millionaire, he was a billionaire.

This *chareidi* businessman had heard about me from

someone and decided to offer me a job in one of his companies. As you can imagine, his offer was a lifesaver. Sure, the monthly salary he was offering was less than what I was used to bringing in. Still, there would be percentages and bonuses that could double what I'd been making before.

So we were pulled back from the brink a split second before we'd have to move. We could continue on as we had before, on the same level we were used to.

I began working for him. He was a tough but fair boss who demanded complete loyalty, honesty, and transparency. Though he was a person who, despite his enormous wealth, didn't cut any corners when it came to his faith, he didn't get involved in my personal life. However, he did expect me to give my all to the job (which was my own desire as well, because the better I was, the more I earned in percentages of sales and bonuses).

I'd like to add here that a big part of trading is done with countries that aren't exactly democracies, to put it mildly. They're authoritarian regimes run by dictators—but they have commodities you can't get anywhere else in the world. Our boss managed to win the trust of these dictators. The international business he ran made him one of the wealthiest people in the world.

Our company employed hundreds of workers and dozens of executives. It was only natural for us to talk among ourselves, always being careful, of course, not to disclose company secrets, even to each other. That was one of the most important conditions of employment: not to talk and not to give out information.

We watched as even very high earners lost their jobs because they made the stupid mistake of talking unnecessarily, whether it was bragging about a deal they'd made or talking about a business transaction they'd gotten wind of.

Given that, we only allowed ourselves to talk about things everyone knew, like how many billions our boss had or the latest news about his private life.

Since he was *chareidi* and none of us were, we were curious to know whether he really kept mitzvos in line with the way he presented himself or if it was all an act. (Every *chareidi* should know that secular people scrutinize their behavior looking to see how sincerely religious they are—and they can tell the truth from the lie.)

Over the years, we saw various proofs that he really was a sincerely *chareidi* Jew who didn't cut any corners when it came to religion. We saw him in all kinds of situations in all kinds of countries, places where no one could see him and situations where there was no choice, and in all of them, he acted like a *chareidi* Jew. He never took off or hid his *kippah* or tzitzis, even in places where the rest of us thought he'd be better off hiding them.

He lived a relatively low-key life. He fit in seamlessly with his neighborhood in a *chareidi* city. Yes, he had a beautiful, spacious home, but he didn't live in an exclusive area, and he didn't conduct himself like the wealthy man he was. To a casual observer, he appeared to be a regular *kollel* guy in all ways, perhaps even more self-effacing and soft-spoken than most.

It was a stark contrast to the tough, decisive businessman we workers knew him to be, and it never ceased to amaze us.

You know something? We admired him.

One day a few of us managers were sitting and talking, and

someone threw out the famous saying, "Every man has his price."

Among us was a *dati* manager who said, "That doesn't apply to everyone. A G-d-fearing person won't transgress a mitzvah for all the money in the world."

We began arguing.

He claimed the Torah says a person is permitted to transgress a mitzvah if it's a case of life or death, except for three prohibitions to which "let him die and not transgress" applies. He also said there might be some religious people who might be tempted to transgress for money, but when it came to Shabbat, for instance, people wouldn't desecrate Shabbat even for a lot of money, except for very weak people who aren't really G-d-fearing.

We didn't accept that. "Talk is cheap," we told him, "but for a million dollars, you'll find people who will do it."

He stood his ground. "No way.

We raised the price (in our conversation, of course, not in reality) to ten million, and then to one hundred million, and then to a billion.

He didn't budge. "A G-d-fearing person won't desecrate Shabbat for all the money in the world."

"Easy for you to say in theory," we told him. "But it would never happen in real life."

The argument stuck in my mind, but never for a minute did I imagine it would become part of my reality.

But then, one Shabbat, it did.

Due to my many sins, I got a phone call one Friday night from the deputy to an African ruler, one of the biggest, who had a trading relationship with my boss worth billions. I'd never spoken to him, only to his subordinates.

"I need to talk to your boss," he said.

I couldn't get a word out of my mouth. If I said the wrong thing, it might enrage him and ruin the business relationship. How could I tell him my boss doesn't use the phone on Shabbat?

"He's not here," is what I said.

"I know he's not there," the man said, "and I also know he doesn't use the phone on Shabbat. But we've got an emergency over here, and the king wants to talk to him."

"Uh...um... Look, I can call him, but he won't answer the phone."

I heard voices, and then the phone was passed to the king himself.

"We know you live in ____ (he said the name of my town) and your boss lives in ____ (he said the name of the *chareidi* city my boss lives in). We called you for a reason. We tried calling him, but his phones are off. We know he doesn't talk on Shabbat, so we're calling you. Go to his house and tell him to pick up the phone because we've got an emergency that puts everything at risk."

I was shaking. "Your Majesty," I said to him, "I have strict orders from my boss never to disturb his Shabbat no matter what and—"

"But now," he thundered furiously, "my instructions to you are to go to his house and tell him I know he's strict about Shabbat, but he has to understand that if I call him, it means there's a big danger. More than that, I can't say."

"Okay, Your Majesty," I said. "I'll contradict his orders this time to follow yours. I'm going right now."

And I did.

I left my house and drove at breakneck speed to my boss's town. What usually takes me half an hour took me only fifteen minutes due to the empty roads.

I got as close to his house as I could with the car and then ran the rest of the way.

It was eleven-thirty at night.

I knocked on the front door. Two minutes later, a boy who looked to be about twelve answered.

"I have to speak with your father," I said.

He shrugged and went to call his father.

As soon as my boss saw me, he knew I hadn't come to taste the cholent. "What's wrong?"

I told him about the phone call from the African ruler.

He was shocked. I could see the wheels turning in his mind.

"But he knows I don't talk business on Shabbos. Why is he even trying?" he asked.

"He told me to tell you he knows you don't talk business on Shabbat, but despite that, he's asking you to call him because of the danger."

My boss closed his eyes for a minute that, to me, seemed like forever.

"Look," he said, "I can't call this a matter of life or death. I'm here, and so are my wife and children. He can't harm us. There's no justification here for desecrating Shabbos."

"But...but maybe there's a coup taking place down there, and you're about to lose all your money."

For that, he didn't need to close his eyes. "There's no justification for desecrating Shabbos for money," he said.

"It's not only money," I said, trying to convince him. "It's your livelihood, and all the money you donate. I've heard you give millions to charity every month."

He looked at me and gave a bitter laugh. "Nice try," he said. "I like the part about the donations. You know my soft spots. But, sorry to tell you this, it's not happening."

I was shaking with fear. I don't know what was going through my mind. You probably think I was worried about my job, but I didn't need to take it that far. The thought of the powerful ruler who controlled a big chunk of my boss's fortune, if not all of it, and who was asking for such a small thing (in my eyes) and yet my boss was stubbornly refusing, sent me into a panic. I felt like I was watching someone tempt fate.

"But," I persisted, "isn't there some kind of allowance in the Torah for over a billion dollars?"

He didn't even answer me. He just laughed, to make it clear I must be kidding.

And then he started to speak his thoughts aloud. "Actually, there's a Rav who lives not far from here. I can ask him."

"Great!" I said. "If there's a question, you ask a Rav."

"But I'm not even going to ask," he told me.

"What? Why not?!" I asked. "Why?!"

The answer he gave me right then is one I'll never forget. "When a Jew wants to find a leniency, he goes to ask a Rav. But I'm not looking for any leniencies. I wasn't born chareidi, I chose it. I grew up completely secular and became religious when, believe it or not, I switched channels and somehow got the Hidabroot program. I saw a chareidi man and was about to switch to a different program, but he said one sentence that made me stay and listen the whole night. He said, 'You're not doing anyone else a favor by becoming religious. You're doing yourself a favor. And if you don't believe that, you'll never be religious even if you wear a kippah and grow a beard.'

"Everything I knew about religion flew out the window. As a businessman, I wondered about what he'd said. Maybe I *was* losing out—or maybe not. It was worth checking.

"I watched dozens of hours of talks. Then I told my wife about it, and both of us pursued our interest in religion, eventually becoming full-fledged *chareidim*. Today, my wife and I have a large family. With each passing day, we're increasingly aware that becoming religious was not only the best thing we ever did but a lifesaver. Now our lives are filled with meaning and purpose.

"You are coming here with an argument that doesn't speak to me. You want me to ask a Rav so I can circumvent Shabbos, but that's not what I want. What I want is the exact opposite. I don't want to circumvent Shabbos. The whole basis on which I became religious is that I'm not doing anyone a favor but that it's doing *me* a favor. And it's so true.

"Shabbos is the best example," he added. "Every week, I wait expectantly for it. I'm doing someone a favor? Shabbos protects me more than I protect myself. And I'm not talking about business but about my family. Shabbos connects me with my family. It guards the only thing that will be left from all my wealth and seeming successes. It's the only success that will be everlasting. Right now, you interrupted me when I was testing my son on what he'd learned this week. All I want is to sit there with him. I'm not the least bit interested in any ruler except the King of Kings, HaKadosh Baruch Hu."

"Wow!" I said to him. "What a story." I was stunned. My boss had never shared any of his personal life with me before. Never would I have dreamed a random program on Hidabroot would cause such a major transformation.

"But what should I do now?" I asked him.

"I forbid you to call him regarding my interests," he told me.

"I can't tell you what to do. I'm only your boss. I can only recommend you not answer him. But if you're afraid of not answering him and you do decide to answer him, tell him I wasn't home and my family didn't know where I was. We won't antagonize him, but he can't talk to me on Shabbos."

He thanked me, and I started to walk away. He called me back and said, "I'm asking you to please not desecrate Shabbos for anything relating to me. It causes me a lot of anguish. I give you my word that I will never do you any harm, *chalilah*, or come to you with any complaints if you refrain from coming to me on Shabbos. You can always say, for the sake of peace, that you went to my house and I wasn't home. *Shabbat shalom.*"

I left there deep in thought.

I told my wife and kids what had happened and said, "I admire him, and I'm really jealous. He's sitting and testing his son on what he's learned, and he has a lot of children, while my son has to beg me to put the phone away." Tears sprang to my eyes. "I want to think about what we should do about it."

Saturday night, the dictator called my boss, furious. I don't know what my boss said to him or how he resolved it. All I know is business hasn't stopped. And if you ask me, the dictator's dependence on my boss has only become greater. If I were in his place, I'd value a person who was ready to throw his business away for religious principles.

As for me, the story changed everything for me and my family. At first, it was just a matter of Shabbat. My wife and I decided to devote Shabbat to the kids. No phones. No screens. Nothing.

We spent some time getting to know Hidabroot and sharing

it with our children. I figured whatever is good for my boss the billionaire would be good for me, too.

As time went on and we heard more, my wife and I realized our plan wouldn't last too long if we didn't anchor it to something bigger than ourselves—to the belief that everything is from G-d, all the good we have, life itself. Slowly we began to become more religious. Today, though we're not what you'd call *chareidi*, we keep Torah and mitzvos, pray, wear a *kippah*. We transferred our children to a religious school founded by Rav Shteinman, *ztz"l*.

Meanwhile, we're still here, in our community. But it looks like we won't be here too much longer. We've got a long road ahead of us, but now, at least the direction is clear.

There's a big, strong light that guides us and illuminates our way. An endless light. The light of Shabbos.

"The Gentleman"

This is a story about a shul so outstanding that everyone who hears about it will wish they could daven in such a place.

It's more than a place of prayer. It's a place of belonging, where everyone is part of one big happy family.

And, as in many families, people are affectionately known by a nickname.

So when the shul member known as "The Gentleman" acts out of character, people do more than just raise their eyebrows in dismay.

For the past thirty years, I've been a member of a shul that's known as a Yekke shul, though not a single one of us traces his ancestry back to Germany.

Ninety-five percent of our members have been regulars for twenty years or more. Naturally, we all know each other very well, from dates of each one's celebrations, the names of their *mechutanim*, family birthdays, and, *lehavdil, yahrtzeit* dates.

Over time, certain nicknames have stuck to each of us, our fond way of relating to one another.

One of us is called "the Gvir." Not because he's wealthy, but because he gives a hundred shekels for each *aliyah* he receives. So the name stuck.

Another is called "the Yekke." He's as punctual as a quartz clock, arriving at shul at exactly five to seven, not a minute before or after.

One is called "the Milkman" because he likes to make coffee and tea for everyone.

The person whose story I want to tell you is called "the Gentleman."

He's called that because he acts like a distinguished person. For instance, you'll never hear him raise his voice. His movements and conversation are calm and pleasant, his beard is always neat, and his clothing is nothing short of impeccable, giving him a majestic appearance.

And another thing: You'll never catch him talking on his cell phone in the street. People have gotten used to the phenomenon, but there are still those for whom a phone conversation in public is considered ill-mannered and shameful, almost like going to a park, lighting a small fire, roasting meat over it, and then eating it in front of a hundred strangers. I know lots of people won't understand what I'm talking about, but there are still some who wouldn't dream of doing things like eating meat in a public place or conducting a phone conversation on the street.

Both groups will understand why he was called "The Gentleman."

One day, the Gentleman arrived in shul bearing refreshments.

We were all curious, because everyone knew his *yahrtzeit* dates and whether any joyous family events were in the offing. What was with the cakes and drinks?

The Gentleman explained that he was traveling to the States for a friend's wedding. We always marked such separations— even if they were for only a few days—with cake and a little schnapps, along with our best wishes for a safe and pleasant journey.

He told us all he was returning Wednesday night.

Thursday arrived, but the Gentleman didn't show up in shul.

Nor did he appear on Friday, Shabbos, or Sunday.

Some people tried calling him, but his phone has an extension code, which he didn't give to just anyone, and calling his home phone was a bit uncomfortable. So we waited, not so patiently. He wasn't the Yekke, but we knew him to be an organized person. If he hadn't returned when he said he would, there had to be a good reason.

When he still hadn't returned to shul by Monday morning, one of our members made an announcement.

"He did travel to a wedding as he told us, but there was another reason for the trip as well, and only I know what it is. All I can say is that everything's okay."

We pressed him to disclose the secret, and he finally gave in.

"I'll tell you the truth. You know I have a son graduating eighth grade, and you know he failed the entrance exam to the top yeshivah of his choice. I told this to the Gentleman, and he told me the friend getting married in the States was a major donor to this yeshivah, and he would ask him to use his influence to get them to accept my son.

132

"I don't know what he did, because we haven't been in touch. All I know is that on Thursday, the yeshivah called to say they'd 'reconsidered' my son's application, and they'd come to the conclusion that he is an excellent *bachur*. Therefore, they told me, they have decided to accept him into the yeshivah. I realized the Gentleman had kept his promise and had arranged for someone with powers of persuasion to convince the yeshivah how important it was to accept my son."

The plot thickened. Now we were no longer worried but intensely curious.

The Gentleman returned a full two weeks after he'd left.

We gave him a big *shalom aleichem* and planned to wait until after davening to ask him what happened.

But right in the middle of davening, the Gentleman whipped out his phone.

We'd never seen such a thing!

Though this story takes place before the era of smartphones or even kosher phones, even back then, people didn't look at messages in shul. The fact that the Gentleman was using a phone during davening—and not only looking at the screen of his BlackBerry but tapping out messages—came as a huge shock. I can't remember anything as remotely shocking in our shul as seeing one of our members using a phone during davening. And the Gentleman of all people!

One person couldn't contain himself. He saw it as a terrible desecration of Hashem's Name. He surmised that the Gentleman's stay abroad had cost him not only his status as a gentleman but much, much more, ruining him for life.

What do you think he did?

He attacked him verbally.

"One doesn't send messages on the phone during davening. It's neither proper decorum nor acceptable."

The Gentleman signaled with an elegant gesture that he'd explain later, and continued tapping away.

Jaws dropped.

After davening, the Gentleman went to the *bimah* and spoke.

"Since I received a justified rebuke from my friend, in addition to looks no less justified from the rest of the congregation, I'd like to ask everyone to remain while I explain exactly what took place here, so there won't be even the slightest suspicion of *chillul Hashem*."

He called over the gabbai, whipped out his cell phone, and said, "Please read these exchanges aloud."

The gabbai began reading: "In addition to the physical pain, I feel pain as well at seeing my father so distressed. *Baruch Hashem*, my father left half an hour ago, and then I was able to release the emotions I'd held back and cry. After half an hour of crying, I could then find the strength to write to you."

To which the Gentleman had replied: "You can cry in front of your father. It's normal."

The writer answered: "I can't bear to see my strong father, whom I've never seen cry, break down in front of me. Too bad the Rav didn't tell my mother to come with me. It's normal for a mother to cry, and I wouldn't have minded crying in front of her."

All of us had questions, and they were soon answered when the Gentleman spoke.

"I'll tell you the whole story," he said. "On my flight to the States, a father and son sat next to me. They showed me a piece of paper with the name of a hospital written in English and asked me how to get there.

"The boy had been diagnosed with the dreaded disease. It happened after he'd been sick for several months, with no one being able to tell him what the problem was.

"By the time the diagnosis was made, the cancer was at an advanced stage. They were advised to fly immediately to a specific hospital in the United States.

"Since the boy's mother was near her due date, the father took a leave of absence from his job to accompany his son.

"The person who directed them to the hospital in America was Rav Chaim Greineman. He came to their house the day before their flight with a list of everything they'd need to take. Before Rav Greineman left the house, he told them, in these very words, 'All the stringencies of halachah according to the Chazon Ish that you so cherish and strive to fulfill are hereby nullified from the moment you board the plane until you land back here in Eretz Yisrael.'"

"When I saw how they didn't even know how to read the English address," the Gentleman continued, "I realized Hashem had sent me to this wedding, which I wouldn't have gone to if I hadn't been asked to do a big favor for someone I know." (He didn't know that we all knew both the man and the favor he'd done.)

"I told the father, 'I'll take you there.'

"I took them first to the apartment I'd rented. Then I brought them to the hospital. I spoke with the doctors and connected the father and son with Jewish organizations that would help them with kosher food and accommodations. The hospitality of American Jews is exceptional.

"When the treatments began, the son asked to speak with me privately. He explained that he felt uncomfortable talking about his illness and medical care with his father because he felt he was bringing him pain, and he couldn't bear to do that. He asked if he could keep in touch with me to share his feelings.

"Any time we were alone, whenever an opportunity arose, he talked to me about his fears—tremendous fears that are very understandable. He cried a lot and said he allowed himself to cry in my presence but not when his father was nearby because it broke his heart to see his father's deep anguish.

"Now, perhaps, you will understand what happened here. When it's seven in the morning for us, it's midnight for them. His father had just left the hospital to go to sleep, and the boy grabbed the chance to write to me what he was feeling. You surely understand that I couldn't simply say to him, 'Wait until I finish davening,' because if I did, he'd fall asleep without anyone to hear his cries.

"Now that you understand our exchange of messages, you surely have no suspicions that I would do anything to lessen the *kedushah* of our shul."

There was complete silence in the shul, and then the gabbai went back up to the *bimah* and said, "I admit it. I, too, had some uncharitable thoughts about our friend the Gentleman. I was wrong. Not only did the Gentleman help the boy and his father, but he stayed there in the States for two whole weeks to do so, far longer than his original plan. I think it's only right for all of us here to commit ourselves to become involved as well, especially since we were guilty of suspecting the innocent."

One person immediately volunteered to raise money for the family, another said he would contact medical organizations, a third and a fourth promised to keep in touch with the boy, a fifth with the father, and others took it upon themselves to help the boy's brothers and sisters.

The gabbai kept us there until every single one of us had committed to contribute in some way.

We sprang into action. Within a few days, contacts were made to consult the best doctors and to arrange a closer, more comfortable place for the father to stay. A professional was called in to help the boy process what he was going through. Organizations stepped in to help at home and to help the family financially while the father wasn't working. Everything was taken into consideration.

Our shul supported the boy for two full years until he experienced a complete recovery. A year later, he got engaged.

It goes without saying that all of us helped with wedding expenses.

And guess where the final and most spectacular *sheva brachos* was held? That's right. Right here in our shul.

One of the speakers was—who else?— the Gentleman.

He lavished praise on the groom for the way he coped with his illness and attributed his recovery to the way he honored his parents and tried not to cause them suffering or distress.

At the end of his remarks, he said, "I want to read you a few lines the boy wrote to me on the day I had to correspond with him in shul in the middle of davening.

"'I just noticed that I'm bleeding,' he wrote me. 'When I looked to see why, I saw it was because I bit my lips to hold back my tears so my father wouldn't cry and feel sad.'

"That's our *chassan*," the Gentleman said. "Someone so devoted to honoring his father will certainly be a devoted husband to his wife. Just as his virtues saved him from all evil, may he merit to establish a true and faithful Jewish home and fulfill his wish to bring his parents *nachas.*"

The crowd was moved to tears. No one there will ever forget those moments.

Almost seventeen years have passed since then. The boy and his wife are parents of a beautiful family, and every so often he visits our shul because of the connection he has with all of us.

If the shul had rare *achdus* before this story, after it, an unbelievable bond formed between each and every member—just as if we were joined as a real family.

The message of this story is that if you see your friend doing something questionable, stop for a minute to judge him favorably.

I think back to those tense moments when I watched the Gentleman sending messages on his phone during davening, and I can't forget the wave of disapproval that washed over me and everyone else there. And just think, this was toward a person we'd known for decades as an impeccable human being. How did we fall like that?

Nowadays, when we know he did the right thing, we realize how important it is for a person to get used to overcoming his initial critical view and instead to judge favorably.

One final message. I suggest everyone try to model their shul after ours. Let it be a place of friendship, love, peace, and brotherhood.

Trapped!

When we hear about the rescue of a Jewish woman from an Arab village, we're sure such a tragedy only happens in dysfunctional families.

It turns out the danger is much closer than we thought.

My life story destroys many myths. I was not born into a disadvantaged, struggling family that was falling apart. I didn't grow up in a development town or a slum. I was born into a warm, good family—one with a little *yichus*, in *chareidi* terms—and I grew up in a nice *chareidi* neighborhood in Yerushalayim.

Until seminary, I was a great girl. Not innocent, but definitely conventional and meeting all expectations.

At the beginning of the school year, I came down with some kind of superbug that kept me in bed for a long time. I had to find some way to fill the long weeks of boredom. A well-meaning, more "open" neighbor gave me a tablet, and I went online to fill the time.

I'll skip the next few months and just say that after I got back on my feet, the teachers saw I wasn't the same girl. Soon the seminary notified me that despite their understanding of and sympathy for the months of illness that kept me home, I did not currently fit the character of the seminary.

During this time, I was up all night, doing whatever I was doing online, and slept all day.

One day I got a personal message from one of the sites I was a member of. It was from a woman, inviting me to an unforgettable experience: a chance to visit an Arab village in Israel.

It didn't occur to me to accept the offer. Go into an Arab village alone? Put myself in the lion's den—an Arab home?

But then followed a lot of explanations about how I was living with a lot of misconceptions about Arab villages, and how there are villages, like the one I was invited to, that are perfectly safe, and I could even check it out. How it was a village friendly toward Israel, and there'd never been a single act of terrorism that originated there. What's more, she was organizing a meeting with three other religious girls who had joined, so I wouldn't be alone. She gave me their names and phone numbers and suggested I contact them. It was going to be a fabulous experience. Only a few minutes' drive, and we'd get a firsthand experience of a kind of life light-years away from the life we knew.

I agreed.

✑   ✑   ✑

Ten months later.

My parents long ago forbade me to enter the house. I have

140

good friends in the village, and I spend many nights there, enjoying the pleasant atmosphere and interesting conversations.

Four months after I started going there, one of the girls introduced me to her brother Salim. He was a nice guy who worked not far from my home in Ramat Shlomo (or, to be more accurate, my former home). He worked with *chareidim* and was very familiar with the *chareidi* community. It was interesting to hear his take on them as an outsider.

Five months later.
The news that we moved in together reached my parents, and they told me through someone who was still in contact with me that as far as they were concerned, I didn't exist. It was as if they'd never had a daughter named Ayali. My friend said she heard they sat shivah for me.

Three years later.
Our house is too small for a family of six—my two children and another Arab woman with one child. Salim and his parents decided to buy a large villa in an Arab village up north. It's a three-story villa. The lower floor will be for Salim's parents, and the two upper floors will be for us and for the family of Ismael, Salim's brother.

And here's where my story actually begins:
We move into the top floor, over Ismael and his three wives. Already on the first day, I hear screams of a certain kind. Based on my own bitter experience, I know the cause right away. One of the wives must be Jewish.

Over the next few days, I get to know Shir and her five

children. I see the terrible hatred from Ismael's other wives toward Shir and the humiliation and bullying she undergoes daily, hourly, and minute by minute.

Shir is in a bad state emotionally. I never see a smile on her face except when once a month, a very large package arrives from Salim and Ismael's grandmother. The package is shipped from an address in Jordan and contains a box for each of the women, with baby clothes, children's games, and gifts for us, the women. Every new garment Shir gets for one of her boys, every candy or toy she can give them, fills her with happiness.

Shir and I become close. We support each other and give each other hope. Shir constantly tells me she wants to run away but is afraid for the children. I, on the other hand—and I know you won't be able to understand this—don't want to run away, for one simple reason.

I have nowhere to go.

I have nowhere to go back to. No family, no friends, and no in the world who knows me and will agree to help. I mean, my family has already told me that as far as they're concerned, I don't exist.

A year later, Shir tells me, her eyes shining, that she's escaping. A certain organization has agreed to rescue her and all five of her children. She tells me I have to come, too.

I'm happy for her, but sad for myself because now I'll be here all alone. Still, I refuse to join her.

Six in the morning. Ismael and Salim wake me up wildly.
"Where are they?"
"You'd better tell us right now where she ran off to!"

I realize Shir managed to escape, and from that moment on, my life turns into Gehinnom.

The whole family blames me. Not a single person in the village believes that the Jewish woman who stole the children didn't tell the other Jew.

From that morning on, Salim decides he isn't taking any chances. From then on, I am forbidden to leave the house alone. Before going out, I have to first get his permission, and I can only leave if I'm accompanied by one of the wives. I'm not allowed to have a cell phone or to contact anyone outside the family.

I'm a prisoner on our floor. When Salim is at work, his parents are home, and there is no way to get down to the ground floor and leave without being caught.

Things are now unbearable. I want to run away so badly, but I missed my chance.

In these days of darkness, I start to pray. In every spare moment—and in "jail" there are plenty of those—I cry out to Hashem and beg Him to take me out of there, to help me get the kids out, to find someplace to go and someone who will agree to take me.

A few weeks after Shir escapes, it looks like Ismael has calmed down, and life is back on track. Then one evening, I see all the men in the family sitting with a stranger who I later learn is an Israeli Arab lawyer. Each time I approach, they whisper suspiciously.

At the end of their meeting, I'm called into the room by Salim and Ismael, and now for the first time I hear about the plan they've been working on for the past three weeks, and about the awful part I'm supposed to play in it.

Ismael is unable to forgive the "kidnapping," and he's devised a plan to take revenge on the people who helped Shir escape.

As a first step, I'm forced to call Shir's parents, asking them to tell her that Ayali is looking for her and she should call me at one in the morning so we can talk.

At one exactly, the phone rings. "Ayali?" a hesitant voice is heard from the speaker. I hold one phone, and on the extension are Ismael and Salim, listening to every word.

"Yes, it's me. How are you, Shir?"

Shir bursts into tears—maybe from excitement, maybe from fear, and maybe because of the memories that flood her. Whatever, Ismael has no patience.

"Say you want to escape, too," he writes on a note.

I say it. Do I have any choice?

Shir answers with a mixture of tears and joy in her voice. "I've been waiting every day to hear you say that."

"Ask how the people came to rescue her," Ismael writes.

"And tell her to tell them that she knows you and that you need to be rescued," Salim adds.

Shir gives me names and phone numbers.

The very next morning, Ismael and Salim, along with three other men, appear in my room, eager to begin the program.

Ismael approaches me threateningly, hissing, "Let it just be clear. One wrong word to Shir and not only will you stay in bed forever, but your two little Jews will, too."

And Salim? Salim nods his agreement. He is ready to sacrifice his own sons, to kill his children for revenge.

I'm unable to dial, my hands are shaking so badly, so they dial for me and then listen to every syllable coming out of my mouth.

A woman answers. When she hears what I'm calling about, she asks if she can record the conversation. That way, the rescue team will know every detail about me, my husband, the village, and where I live.

I tell her how bad things are for me, how much I want to escape, how much my children are suffering. I end by begging her to get me out of there.

I meant every word I was saying in this script.

"And as soon as possible. Every day that goes by is dangerous for me here," one of the men writes to me.

We agree that I'll call the next day at the same time. She ends the call with words of encouragement, saying that soon this nightmare will end. She promises that my request will go to the department responsible for rescue and that they'll give my case top priority.

The five men walk out of the room and leave me alone.

I know very well what I'm going to cause.

What should I do? Do I have to give up my life and the lives of my two children and not cooperate?

I stay in bed that day. I don't even get up to eat. I just pray to Hashem to tell me what to do. I'm no longer asking to get out of there. I don't care if I have to stay there and suffer for the rest of my life. I just don't want to draw those good people into a trap.

That evening, ten men from my husband's family gather to meet with the lawyer, and I'll never forget what I hear.

First, I realize it isn't only Ismael who's looking to take revenge. There are four other families from nearby villages where a Jewish woman their son had married was "kidnapped" along with her children. For a long time, there's been rage about these escapes, and everyone is waiting to take revenge.

The Israeli police force is active in our villages. Mostly, they don't interfere with local conflicts. But families know that if a Jew is kidnapped or murdered, it will bring the police and the army out in full force. They're looking for a way to operate that won't get them into trouble if they are caught.

The Arab lawyer quotes them an Israeli law known as the Dromi Law. What he says is engraved on my heart:

"No person shall bear criminal responsibility for an act that was immediately necessary in order to repel someone who breaks into or enters a home...with the intent of committing a crime, or someone who attempts to break into or enter the above."

Based on that, the lawyer advises them to get the rescuers to enter their homes and take the children. That way, under Israeli law, it would be very difficult to convict them. The lawyer goes on to explain that there is a paragraph in the law that says this will not apply "if the act was reasonable under the circumstances in order to repel the intruder or enterer." He adds, "As in this case."

I can't bear to listen anymore.

They're going to work it out so that everything is legal!

I'm torn to shreds.

The next day, Salim and Ismael meet again, this time with men I've never seen before. I'm given a page with clear instructions on what to say.

When I call, I can sense they've been waiting for my call. They're ready with information about the village, but want to know my husband's work schedule and more information about the village roads, which they haven't been able to get themselves. We talk for a few more minutes about various matters concerning me, the age of the children, and their condition.

"Say you can't carry two kids by yourself, you need their help to take them out of the house," they write me.

I say it.

"That's okay," they answer me. "We'll find a time when the

146

house is completely empty and come in on our own. It won't be a problem."

"Call again in five days," they say, ending the call.

Five days later, I'm instructed to say that next Monday, there will be a celebration in the village next to ours to celebrate Rabi' al-awwal, "the first spring." (It's called the first to distinguish it from the fourth month, Rabi' al-akhar, which is the second spring.) I'm told to tell them that the whole family is going and the house will be empty. I'm to say I'm not feeling well and need to stay home with my two kids. We can't lose out on such a good opportunity. That's what I'm told to say.

Friday morning, I call again to hear what the plans are. The rescue organization asks for more details about the layout of the house, and I decide this is my last chance to try to save them.

"The entrance to our house is the opposite of east," I say. I mean that the entrance to our house is to the west, *ma'arav*. When spelled with an *ayin*, *ma'arav* means west. When spelled with an *aleph*, it sounds the same, but it means ambush. That's the warning I'm trying to give them.

They don't understand. I use the expression "the opposite of east" again and again, but they don't get it. Salim is getting impatient and signals me not to say those words again. Maybe he feels I'm forcing them into the conversation, and he's afraid they contain a code.

I never talk to Shir again. Ismael has no interest in my calling her, and she herself would never call the phone in the house she's run away from. Also, the rescue organization says they haven't told her because they only tell the people who need to know. The operation has to remain secret.

Monday morning. The house fills with a lot of men. Some I

recognize from family gatherings; some are complete strangers. They bring in all sorts of weapons—like iron rods and anything that can be used to hit with.

They decide that some of them will wait inside the house in an inner room while some will hide in the storage shed and wait until the rescue forces are inside the house and then lock them in. In addition, more people will wait at the entrance to the village to block the exit of those who will surely be waiting in a car and will try to escape when they realize something has gone wrong.

I'm lying in bed. I can't move a finger. I don't know if I'm dead or alive. Every passing second takes me through the seven levels of Gehinnom. They see that I'm pale and trembling, and it only serves to increase their joy.

"Tonight, you'll see what punishment the Jewish traitors get."

Monday afternoon. Salim, Ismael, and the rest of the household members are getting ready to leave for the neighboring village. They're afraid the rescuers are watching to see if the house is empty and that the family members are at a safe distance.

Someone's knocking on the door. Who could it be? Everyone here comes in without asking permission.

It's Salim's mother, holding a big box—the presents from her mother in Jordan. It always comes on the first of the month. Today the gifts are a little early and come a few hours before it begins (for Muslims too, the day begins at sunset). Maybe the grandmother knows about the plan, too, and is sending a present in advance?

"This time she sent you a bigger box than anyone else," his mother says, as if I can concentrate on a single word she's saying.

"Go ahead and open it. See what you got. It will comfort you."

Trapped!

But I can't move.

She opens the box for me, leaves it open on the bed, and leaves.

I hear the latest preparations for the evening's events and almost lose my sanity.

Do these people who are risking their lives to save a suffering Jewish woman deserve this? This is it? They don't have a chance? There's no way to save them?

Only a few years have passed since I heard that even if a sharp sword is on a person's neck, that shouldn't stop him from asking for mercy. It seems more like hundreds of years ago, but it gives me some hope. I can still pray.

And so...I pray.

Through the tears, I see there's a note in the box. I hadn't noticed it at first. I didn't even know what I was seeing. But after a few minutes, my brain registered it. Something's strange. She never sent a letter before.

I look at the note and see it's written in Hebrew:

Ayali, I don't know if you meant to hint at an ambush or not.

Anyway, I know Ismael, and right from the start, I suspected he'd orchestrated the whole conversation and that you have no way of letting me know because they've taken away your ability to communicate with the outside world. That's why I packed presents like the grandmother in Jordan sends. I wrote her address as the sender and sent it to your house. I made sure my package will arrive a few hours before hers so it won't arouse suspicion and make them open the package that's meant for you.

Maybe I'm overly suspicious because of everything I've gone through, but I'm not taking any chances. Open the baby pants that are in the box. You'll find a cell phone with a

149

SIM card hidden inside it. In the contacts list are my number
and that of the organization that rescued me.
  If I got it right, then just warn these wonderful people.
  I hope it's all my imagination and false fears.
Shir

I immediately call the number in the contacts and whisper, "Tell them not to come. It's a trap."

Just then, the door opens, and I slide the phone behind the bed. In that split second, Ismael could have spotted the cellphone, but thank G-d he didn't. He just looks at me suspiciously and says in Arabic, "Today we're settling accounts."

He walks out and slams the door behind him.

I'm terrified. I don't even dare look for the cellphone. I'm too scared they'll hear the noise of my heavy bed moving. I'm just hoping someone listened to the call, and it didn't go to voicemail. A feeling of dread fills me.

I have two hours to wait before finding out. These are the tensest hours of my life. I know that if they come and get hurt or killed, everyone will blame me for leading them into the trap. And they'll be right, at least partially. Nobody will believe that I was forced into it. The security forces will take revenge, an awful revenge, but I don't care about that so much. What bothers me is knowing I'll probably go down in the history of the Jewish people as the first Jewish woman to cause the death of Jews. That's what people will know about me for generations, till the end of time. Maybe they'll even teach it in history books.

These thoughts tear at my heart. I find myself praying to the Master of the World, in Whose light I was raised and educated: "From the depths, I call You, Hashem. Please hear my voice and listen to my pleas."

Then comes the next verse: "If You keep a record of iniquities, Hashem, who will stand?"

I'm broken from crying. What a fool I was. What have I done to myself?

The designated time arrives.

And nobody comes.

Tensions rise. All the armed, bloodthirsty men hope it's only a delay.

After a short wait, they tell me to call the rescuers and ask what happened.

The answer I get is that the organization didn't have enough money for the rescue operation, so they called it off.

I breathe a deep sigh of relief.

Ismael, Salim, and the other men explode in anger. They blame me for warning the rescuers and vent their rage at anyone who stands in their way.

Inside, I'm thrilled. Glowing. I won't go down in history as a Jewish woman who betrayed her people, but as a Jewish woman who returned to her roots.

They finally leave me alone. I hear them talking among themselves, saying there was no way I could have warned the rescue organization, and that they had just backed out on their own at the last minute.

How can they know the ways of Providence?

I'll spare you the details of the actual rescue, which took place six weeks later. I coordinated it using the cellphone I'd gotten from Shir, without anyone listening in. That day the whole family went to a cousin's wedding, and I stayed behind, locked in the room. The rescuers actually did have to enter the house. They broke in using burglary tools and rescued me.

Why am I going public with the story now?

To warn about the Internet? I don't think *my* warning is necessary. Anyone alive today would have to be blind not to see how destructive it is. As for the ones who don't want to listen, nothing will help.

Is it to tell you about the power of prayer even when the blade of a sword is on your neck? There are enough stories like that.

There are two reasons why I decided to tell.

The first reason is because of the end of the story, which, for me, is the main point of the story.

Because of my family. My real one. My father and mother, my sisters and brothers, my *saba* and *savta*, and all the other family members.

The day I returned home to an Israeli city, I was taken to an apartment they'd prepared for me. The three of us collapsed onto the beds and woke up in the morning. In the living room, my whole family was waiting. They welcomed us with immense love, despite everything I'd put them through. I'm sure that besides the immense grief of my parents who lost their daughter that way, the step I took affected my family in countless ways, from problems with my siblings' *shidduchim* to the shame I caused my father, to the point where he had to leave his senior position in the yeshivah where he taught.

Despite it all, they forgave me and welcomed us back emotionally with tears of joy. My mother was almost fainting from emotion at having her Ayali come back.

If only I had known all those terrible years that they would welcome me back, my life would have been completely different. I would have known I had somewhere to go back to, that despite everything, I had a family and a father and mother who were always waiting for me.

That's why I beg all parents, and really every member of every family: Do you have a child or sibling who's gone off the *derech*? Were you told to cut off all contact with them? Did you maybe even sit shivah for them? Please, just make sure they know one thing: that they can always come home. Make sure they know you're waiting every minute of the day with open arms and hearts full of love for them to return. And that you're praying and hoping the children will return to their borders.

Now for the second reason I'm telling my story.

I want each and every one of us, even those who went a little bit off the straight path, to always remember, "As a father has mercy on his children, so will Hashem have mercy on us." Even if we moved far away, and it looks like we've lost any connection to our Father in Heaven, still—the minute we return, He's waiting for us and welcomes us with open arms. "Return to Me," Hashem tells us, "and I will return to you."

Facing Life's Storms

*Life creates stories, and stories produce heroes.
Yet rarely, if ever, is there a hero who stars in more
than one story.*

Boaz is that rare hero.

*When you read this, you might find it hard
to believe that one man went through everything
described.*

*But it's all true and documented. Names of peo-
ple and places are not changed.*

*Which makes it one of the most moving stories
I've ever encountered.*

The story begins twenty-eight years ago on 22 Tishrei
5744 / October 4, 1992.

A man from Itamar named Boaz is driving through
Nablus to his place of work at Israpot in Karnei Shomron.

Today, the words "driving through Nablus" are

incomprehensible. Back then, it was a regular part of life. Actually, *until* then.

On the main road opposite the Balata refugee camp, Boaz encounters a human barrier. Hundreds of Palestinians are blocking the road and throwing stones and metal objects. Boaz is caught in the *eye* of the storm.

As this takes place, hundreds more rioters from the nearby Balata refugee camp join the stone-throwers. The mob converges threateningly on Boaz's car.

Boaz smells danger. There have been dozens of terrorist attacks that year—including shooting attacks—that killed many Jews. He calls the police.

The police say they know what's going on, but are unable to disperse the rioters.

It's just Boaz and the mob.

All of a sudden, a man pointing a gun steps out of the crowd and heads straight for Boaz.

Boaz realizes his fate is going to be like that of many before him, but he decides he isn't ready to die without a fight.

He pulls out his 9mm pistol and fires into the air.

The man keeps coming.

Army forces surround the mob, and they, too, begin firing.

And the man with the gun keeps coming.

Boaz fires again. One of the Arabs standing next to the man with the gun falls. Everyone begins to run away, and Boaz takes advantage of the confusion. He steps on the gas and drives straight at the Arab with the gun. The man fires two shots and jumps aside at the last instant to avoid being run over.

Miraculously, Boaz manages to escape the raging mob.

There are cell phones in 1992, but they don't come with a camera.

Boaz is arrested that same day for shooting and causing

injury. The Arab who fell injured his hip. Boaz sits in jail for three days in the Kishon Detention Center, after which he is released, and charges are filed against him.

At his trial, Boaz is represented by Attorney Aryeh Schnitzer. Schnitzer proves to the court that Boaz's life was in real danger. A plea bargain is arranged: Boaz is given a suspended sentence and must pay one hundred thousand shekels to the injured Arab.

Boaz, married and a father, adds another shift to his already long workday. He works from dawn till dusk to support his family and to pay the Arab, one of the would-be murderers.

Ten years pass. In those ten years, the Oslo Accords are signed, and terrorism intensifies. Stone-throwing escalates into terrorist attacks on buses. Thousands are killed. The situation in the territories becomes unbearable. Still, Boaz and his family continue to live in Itamar, and Boaz continues to work from early in the morning until midnight to pay off the debt and to support his family.

None of them know the tragic import of Boaz's long workday.

Thursday night, 11 Tammuz 5762 / June 20, 2002. A terrorist infiltrates the settlement of Itamar at 9:00 p.m.

He makes his way to a house, enters the kitchen through the back door, and begins shooting, slaughtering the occupants.

Home at that time is the mother, Rachel Shabo, and her five children. The father, Boaz, the same man we were talking about, is not there to protect them. He's still at work.

Within minutes, the terrorist murders Rachel Shabo and three of her children: Neria (15), Zvika (12), and Avishai (5). Two other children, Avia (13) and Asael (9), found a hiding place. Two older children, Yariv and Atara, are not home at the time.

The community's security unit receives an alert. Yosef Twito (31), commander of the security squad and father of five, is shot and killed by the terrorist, who barricades himself in the house.

A large contingent of IDF and Border Police forces surround the house. Fighting continues for an hour, during which the fighters rescue the injured Asael, who hid in a closet. Later in the fighting, one of the fighters spots 13-year-old Avia signaling to them from a bedroom window.

The fighter runs to the rescue, but the terrorist also hears the movement and runs into the room before him.

Avia crawls under her mother's bed.

The terrorist searches under the bed and finds her.

The fighter storms into the room. The terrorist shoots in Avia's direction, severely wounding her, but he takes a bullet and flees.

The fighter finds Avia and stops the bleeding.

The terrorist escapes through the bathroom window but is eliminated after a brief fight in the yard.

On his way home from work, Boaz hears about "something going on in the community." He watches from afar as his family fights for its life, and though his own life is saved, he sees his beloved family slaughtered, and his world turns black.

His only consolation is his surviving children: Yariv, Atara, Avia, and Asael. Asael is seriously injured during the rescue, and one leg is later amputated. The helicopter that takes him to the hospital returns to take Avia, who is also injured.

Boaz Shabo fights for Asael's life. Once his son is out of danger, Boaz fights to save the boy's other leg.

The broken Shabo family tries to pull themselves together after the terrible tragedy. Boaz now must be both mother and father to his surviving children.

And within this difficult story, a point of light.

Five years pass, and in 5767/2007, Boaz remarries, to Hila, the mother of five children.

When triplets are born to them, they feel that Hashem is returning to Boaz the three children He took from him.

The triplets join Boaz's four children, Hila's five children, and, believe it or not, another child the couple adopts. Together, there are thirteen children in the home.

Asael Shabo, who lost his right leg in the attack, becomes an outstanding athlete, a basketball player and swimmer who represents Israel in the Paralympics.

Boaz's second marriage flourishes due to the special qualities of both spouses.

When we say the marriage "flourishes," that includes the relationships between the children as well. Boaz's four children and Hila's five became close.

And the story is not yet over.

One day in 5771/2011, a letter from the court, addressed to Boaz, arrives at their home.

Boaz opens the envelope and feels faint.

The letter states that the Arab who shot at him in 1992 is suing him in civil court (in addition to the one hundred thousand shekels he'd won in the criminal trial), and his claim has been accepted.

How much did this Palestinian demand and receive?

Two and a half million shekels.

According to the letter, an official was ordered to take possession of Boaz Shabo's home, his salary, and his possessions. In addition, a stay of exit order was issued, prohibiting Boaz from leaving the country.

After the Palestinians destroyed his home and murdered his family, the rioter who'd tried to kill him ten years earlier was now bringing him to financial ruin.

Boaz contacts Chezi Shabak, CEO of ZAKA Israel, a volunteer organization that assists terror victims and their families. They've been there for Boaz since the first attack, helping him with his son Asael's rehabilitation and with the rest of his family, and he needs their help now.

Chezi Shabak refers him to a lawyer in his shul. When the lawyer hears the story, he's so moved that he declares himself willing to represent Boaz pro bono, without charge.

The lawyer's name will be familiar to you, Mr. Walder, and to your readers from previous stories: Moshe Yitzchak Osditcher.

Attorney Osditcher tells Boaz he will file an appeal, but the chance of overturning a court ruling five years after it's been given is extremely slim. At most, he says, he might be able to reduce the excessive amount of compensation awarded.

The appeal is filed. The main thrust of its argument is a request to the court to show mercy by dividing the debt into manageable payments. It's clear that otherwise, Boaz will never get out of his situation.

All that Osditcher can do for his client is ask for an investigation of his ability to pay, which would prove that the man is in debt and unable to support his family, let alone make large debt repayments.

None of the arguments help. Despite the terrible tragedy Boaz and his family went through, the court is determined to squeeze out of him what he doesn't have—even if doing so will cause the complete collapse of the second family he's established.

There seems to be no way out. The lawyer feels unable to look his client in the face (and remember, he took the case pro bono). He then does what he knows how to do best: think outside the box.

After several nights spent reading and rereading the verdict, only to repeatedly discover there's no crack in it that can be used to justify an appeal, he decides to go through all the material again to look for something that isn't written in the indictment, the court proceedings, or the sentence.

At 4:00 a.m., just as he is about to give up, his eyes catch sight of a minor, technical document that practically no one has bothered to take a look at. Something catches his eye. He looks more closely and can hardly believe what he's seeing.

His roar of triumph is almost loud enough to wake the house.

The very next day, Attorney Osditcher files a motion to dismiss. The grounds? "The statement of claim was not duly provided."

Osditcher demands that the (Palestinian) prosecutor, as well as the messenger who delivered the statement of claim, be called to testify before the court so he can question them.

He doesn't tell anyone what he's planning. Not even Boaz. The surprise will be total.

The day in court arrives. Attorney Osditcher questions the messenger about the delivery process.

The testimony of messengers is usually accepted because they are considered neutral parties who have no personal interest in the case and so no reason to lie.

The messenger states that he arrived at Boaz's home address at such and such a time, "and I had the residents sign the summons."

Osditcher shows him the document he delivered, and the messenger confirms it was the one he'd presented and gotten signatures for and says that everything was done in a legal and honest manner.

Osditcher asks him to describe the residence and tell everyone who exactly signed the form.

The judge's patience is wearing thin.

"Attorney Osditcher," the judge says, "bombarding the witness with questions will not help. The document was given, there is a signature here, the messenger has described the house and the signing process. I don't understand why you are wasting the court's time with this."

"Your honor," Osditcher says, "as we've all seen, the messenger did a wonderful job. He was able to find Boaz's house and also have his wife Rachel sign a receipt for the document. This happened on July 15, 2007. But there's a little problem, your honor. Mrs. Rachel Shabo was murdered fifteen years earlier, on April 10, 1992, by a Palestinian murderer who lives not far from the prosecutor. So either the messenger is standing here lying in court, or he managed to climb to the Heavens and get her signature, in which case he's lying under oath about what happened the same way he's lying about the address he gave."

The courtroom erupts.

The judge quickly looks at the document, as do the lawyers for the Palestinian.

No procedure is necessary. Both sides realize the case will be dismissed, which is exactly what happens.

Shabo and Osditcher hug and cry. For Boaz, these moments are packed with all the tension and anguish he's been through.

Now we get to the last part of the story.

Boaz and Hila start all over again, raising the four children rescued from the inferno (one of them with his leg amputated), the five children from Hila's first marriage, the three born to them together, and another son they adopted. Each word written here is a story in and of itself.

Despite years of suffering, poverty, and deprivation, Boaz and Hila run a happy, joy-filled home. How full of happiness, you can learn from these two incredible facts:

Remember Avia? The one who was seriously injured during the terrorist attack and transported by helicopter after Asael?

Well, she married David, her stepbrother, Hila's eldest son from her first marriage.

David works at Ben Gurion Airport, while Hila is the director of the Kedumim Military and Civilian Center.

As if that's not enough, remember the son the Shabos adopted? He married Nachal, Hila's daughter from her first marriage.

What's Boaz's secret? How did he manage to survive these hardships? How did he manage to establish a new home on the ruins of the old one that burnt down—literally—after his family was so brutally slaughtered by a murderer? How did he build another family that lives in such harmony that everyone wants to stay part of it?

The answer can be found in a bag hanging on the wall at the entrance to the family home, the new home, just like in the old one.

People always asked Boaz, as well as his first wife, Rachel, Hy"d, "Why is this bag hanging here?"

They would smile but make no reply.

One day, some years after the disaster that befell him, Boaz was asked to console mourners in the Golan, where two children died in a fire.

Suddenly, without prior notice, he was asked to speak. He'd never spoken in public before. This would be the first time.

Put on the spot like that, he decided to tell them the secret of the bag.

"When a man comes home," Boaz said, "he brings with him all the tensions, worries, fights, arguments, anger, and stress he's accumulated during the day. He walks into the house and hands them to his wife and children.

"But I've always had a bag hanging from a nail at the entrance to my home, a few inches from the mezuzah. Every time I get home, I put in it all the pressures, worries, anger, and quarrels, and walk in to greet my wife and children calm and collected, just like I left them in the morning."

When he told this to me, Boaz added, "That's the message I want you to convey to your readers. Because, like all of us, they struggle with the challenges that life brings them."

I think Boaz's heroic story compels us all to rise to the challenge. If he could build and rebuild a beautiful home filled with joy, love, and pleasantness, each and every one of us can and must.

If you think the story is coming to an end, it isn't. Remember the Palestinian who was injured?

He again filed his claim for two and a half million shekels. This time the delivery was legal.

Now, a difficult process is underway in court, and the amount seems to have dropped dramatically to several hundreds of thousands, both because it has been proven that the Palestinian's level of disability is only 5 percent, and also because the lawyers proved that he was not an innocent bystander but had threatened Boaz's life and therefore was partially at fault.

One of the arguments raised by the judge was the Palestinian's request to "put a lien on the disability allowance received by Asael" (whose leg was amputated).

Boaz was apparently condemned to suffer through not only the terrible tragedy but forced to deal with a humiliating financial crisis that became worse when one of the triplets needed a drug not covered by the HMO at the cost of NIS 7,500 per month.

But Boaz is smiling. And if Boaz is smiling, it's a smile that should encourage all those suffering in the world.

Because if there are ten measures of suffering, Boaz Shabo has gotten nine of them— even if he won't admit it.

Hidden Emotions

A new bride discovers that she and her husband are not going to run their own lives.
Someone else will do it for them.
You've surely heard stories about women and their mothers-in-law.
But never one like this.

M y story begins when I met my husband.
I didn't feel any excitement about meeting him. We were worlds apart, and after the very first meeting, I knew he wasn't for me. I wasn't even waiting to hear if he wanted to continue. But when I told my parents, they said they wanted me to go out with him again. Eli came from a good family, they told me. They'd grown up in the same neighborhood with his family and knew them well.

A week went by before Eli took the trouble to call and say he wanted to continue. I was a little put off. Why did it take him

so long to get back with an answer? But my parents insisted I continue, so I went out with him again.

After several dates, I brought him home for my parents to meet. He brought a big bouquet of flowers, like a real gentleman. That got my parents excited. They saw him as a golden boy from a golden family. Me, less so.

After meeting my parents, he asked me to come meet his. I agreed. I, too, wanted to see the family I knew would be mine in the future. As soon as I set foot in their house, I sensed their disappointment in me. I wasn't at all what they'd expected. They looked at me and saw a quiet religious girl with no airs about her, a girl from an ordinary family with no special lineage and no higher education. Their dreams were shattered.

Now I know that after this meeting his mother put a lot of pressure on him to go out with a different girl, one with a couple of degrees and from the ethnic group she'd dreamed of him marrying. But my husband didn't want to date anyone else. He told his mother, "I like the girl I'm dating, and right now, I'm dating only her."

We dated a long time before deciding to get married. Both sets of parents sat down to discuss finances and to set a date for the wedding. I wasn't happy with the date they chose, but I respected my parents' wishes. I knew he was a good boy from a good family.

My parents wanted to hold the engagement party in our shul's hall, but his parents objected that it wasn't elegant enough. They were willing to pay, but it had to be in a regular hall.

His parents chose the hall and the band. My parents and I didn't interfere. After all, who were we? Just simple people who weren't paying. We made only one small request: to have the traditional trays of cookies, which is an integral part of every henna party. But they adamantly refused.

"It's not sophisticated," they said. "It's downright barbaric, something from the middle ages."

Like guests, all that was left for us to do was to pick what we'd wear.

When I was shopping for a dress, I saw one that was turquoise with lace trim. I could just see myself in it.

When I told my mother-in-law about the dress, I received my first command.

"Absolutely not," she said. "No one wears that today. Wear white. Turquoise is out of style."

I gave in because I was taught to respect. I told my parents about the conversation with my mother-in-law. I thought they'd take my side, but they said we needed to defer to their wishes, especially since they were paying, and so I should buy a white dress as my mother-in-law asked.

My aunt, though, couldn't believe it.

"By no means should you let her take control of your life from now on in," she told me. "If you want to show respect, wear a white dress—but add three green flowers to show her that while you will respect her wishes, you will also make sure to express your own."

Naturally, I was too afraid to do that.

I came to my engagement party wearing a dress that wasn't my taste and jewelry my mother-in-law chose, not me, because, after all, I was a girl from the middle ages and definitely wouldn't pick something fashionable. She made sure to go by herself and buy what she liked.

I felt people were controlling me. Worse, I was upset with

myself for not doing what was good for me and for not fighting for my wishes. I was entitled to, no?

I'd always dreamed of a certain wedding gown. Whenever I passed by the store window, I'd think to myself, *There's my gown.*

Finally, the moment came to step into my dream. I went to the bridal salon and tried on the gown, enjoying every minute of it.

A month before the wedding, my mother-in-law told me she wanted to come see the gown. I agreed. Why not? If she wanted to see the wedding gown I'd be wearing, let her. But I never expect such a reaction.

"This? It's so plain!" she cried. "We have important guests coming. The gown needs to be more elegant."

She told the dressmaker to totally remake the dress from scratch.

All my dreams of wearing that dress flew out the window. Are you wondering why I agreed? It's because I wanted to honor her.

The biggest moment of my life arrived—the moment every girl hopes and dreams of.

Was I excited? Not really. My wedding wasn't exactly the wedding of my dreams.

I didn't pick the hall or the orchestra. I had no say about the color scheme or the menu. They wanted the very best, so naturally, I wasn't the address. They certainly weren't going to take me around to help them choose because I certainly wouldn't pick the right things, the perfect things a bride should choose.

I arrived at the hall like a guest, looking around and waiting to be led to the bride's chair on which I was supposed to sit. The chair was disappointing, too. It wasn't a chair but a swing, which meant anyone who felt like it could sit next to me—or, to be more exact, on the veil, tugging it in all directions. I don't remember all that much about the wedding. What I do remember is that I didn't know how to dance to the music the band was playing. It wasn't a style I knew or liked. The food on the tables didn't look all that amazing, either. All in all, though, it looked like everyone had a good time.

The wedding ended. We drove to a new apartment that belonged to my in-laws. They were letting us live in it until they sold it.

It was a brand-new apartment, just built. Five large rooms plus a big balcony. We were overjoyed.

I walked into the bedroom, and my heart sank. It wasn't the bedroom set I'd chosen, but the one my mother-in-law had picked. As usual, she paid, so she was the boss who chose everything.

A month after the wedding, I was expecting. We were so happy. I suggested to my husband that we move so we wouldn't have to move in the ninth month if his parents decided to sell the place then.

When my mother-in-law heard this, she got annoyed. "She's acting like a child. We told you you can stay here until we sell the apartment, so what's the problem? Relax. We won't ask you to leave soon. Besides, there's no buyer right now."

"You might even make the brit in the building's hall," my father-in-law added.

Feeling we had no choice, we stayed in the apartment, though I wasn't comfortable with the decision. I knew we couldn't rely on what they said.

My siblings couldn't get over the apartment, both because of its size and because it had all the latest features. "You got a new apartment," they'd say enviously. And I would give a crooked smile and say, "Money isn't everything in life."

I was in my fifth month when I got a message from my moth-er-in-law that realtors would be showing the apartment in the coming days. The apartment I lived in.

Realtors knocked on the door continually, bringing in poten-tial buyers and giving them a tour of the place.

One evening, there was a knock at the door. When I opened, I was startled to see a couple and their dog standing there. They'd come to see the apartment. I asked them if they could please put the dog on the balcony, but they refused. "He wants to see the apartment, too."

After they left, I went into the bedroom and saw nail scratches on the bed frame. I was mad at myself. *Why is this happening to me? Why am I such a pushover? Why don't I stand up for my rights? If I had insisted on their not bringing the dog into the bedroom, I wouldn't have caused myself this grief.*

One day, early in the morning, I went into the city for a routine checkup, and while I was out, I got a call from my husband. "Please stay home today. A realtor will be bringing someone to see the apartment."

"Fine," I said. "But not in the morning, because I'm not home."

I ended the call, and after a few minutes, he called again, furious. "My mother said we're ungrateful. Isn't it enough that she gave us the apartment? Why are we paying her back with bad?"

I started to cry. What had I done that was so bad? I had an important appointment with the doctor. I didn't know ahead of time that they were supposed to come.

At noon, I arrived home at the same time as my husband. We put the key in the lock only to see that the door was already open.

We walked in, and who did we see? My father-in-law and

mother-in-law making themselves at home on the couch, with the realtor and clients.

This time I was really furious. With all due respect to this being their apartment and them having a key, I had the right to know who entered the apartment. After all, I had personal belongings that I didn't want anyone to see or touch.

It was a very stressful time for me, especially since I felt no one understood me.

For Shabbos, we went to my in-laws. They had me wash heavy ceramic serving dishes and baking trays. They claimed that my condition was not an illness and that I should continue as usual.

I felt like a hired maid. My mother-in-law would tell me how she had always left her mother-in-law's house spotless. She'd wash the dishes and the floor, even picking up the dining room chairs and putting them on the table, and only then leave.

Sometimes when I stood next to her as she washed dishes, she liked to give me a dig by saying, "Look how shiny my pots are. It drives me crazy to see the pots of the _____ (here she'd say the name of my ethnic group). They're so dirty."

Needless to say, my in-laws would not eat anything in my house. They only drank water in a paper cup. After all, I'm from a dirty ethnic group.

One Shabbos, we went with them to a hotel, and I got another dig. "Why don't you wear pretty tunics like other young women? You dress like an old lady."

The truth is, I was shocked by that remark. *What do you care what I wear? Every woman has her own style. The same way I don't comment on what you wear, don't you comment on what I wear.* Naturally, I didn't dare tell her that. I just lowered my head, went to my room, and burst into tears. I couldn't take what she'd said.

When I was in my eighth month, the message came: "The apartment has been sold. Start moving out your things."

But you promised we could stay in the apartment and even make a brit here, I heard a choked voice inside me say. *When I wanted to move eight months ago, you said I was a baby and took things too hard.*

I began packing.

The move was horrible. One morning, in the middle of moving, I felt intense pain. I went to the hospital alone because my husband had to stay with the movers. They put me on a monitor to make sure everything was okay. I looked at the ceiling and asked myself, *What am I doing here? I'm not in the right place.* As if it were in my hands.

I was in touch with my husband to let him know what was happening and to hear how things were going at the apartment.

After several hours, I was discharged from the hospital and warned not to exert myself.

I went straight to the small place we'd rented.

I don't need to tell you how traumatic it was for me to go from a large luxury apartment to a tiny, stuffy unit. And this is before we had the baby.

We had to get rid of most of our furniture because what filled five rooms was way too much for one and a half rooms. The move went well, but my mother-in-law had more to say.

"The place was full of dust," she said accusingly. "Couldn't you clean the place before you left? You were given a new apartment, and that's how you return it?"

I wanted to explain to her that after coming home from the hospital, it was hard to clean the apartment. My husband volunteered to tell her instead, but nothing helped. I was still to blame.

172

The unit was located in the courtyard of a kindhearted older woman's home. I used to sit with her, and we'd talk.

◢   ◢   ◢

Baruch Hashem, we were blessed with a son. Talk started about where to make the brit. Again, I was pushed to the side, not part of it. I thought about having it in the shul's hall, but my in-laws were against it. They decided to pay more and have it in the same hall where we got engaged. Did I feel it was the brit ceremony of my own son? I can't say I felt that way.

They dressed the baby in the strange clothes they use at a brit. My mother-in-law took him from me and gave him to people we had nothing to do with. They passed the baby from hand to hand, and in every picture, instead of seeing me and my husband, she's there. I couldn't feel happy. True, they paid for most of it, but the baby was mine, and he was worth more than all their money.

◢   ◢   ◢

When we came for Shabbos with the baby, I took an afternoon nap in the room and overheard her conversations with my husband. "What kind of a wife do you have? How can you get along with her? She doesn't take care of you. She doesn't respect you. She's domineering. And you listen to everything she says! Why? Don't you have a mind of your own?"

These words entered his heart, and every so often, he'd remind me of how right his parents were. Our relationship was rocky. There was a lot of distance between us. I didn't trust him. I felt that he sided with his parents, not me. Instead of the plant growing and flourishing, it was weak and rotten at its root.

Our son grew, and from time to time, we would leave him with my mother-in-law. When we'd come to pick him up, he'd be dressed differently. "The clothes you dress him in aren't appropriate! My grandchild will not go around looking like that. I used to dress Eli in a suit with a bow tie. He looked well-dressed and neat."

Our lives continued. On the surface, everything was quiet. But inside, I was burning up and withdrawn, while they were running our lives and making sure to put me down constantly.

Where was my husband in all this? I guess he was okay with it. He wasn't even aware of the damage made by such comments.

A few months later, we had good news again. But the joy was mixed with sadness. I felt that my husband didn't know what I was going through with my mother-in-law. I used to cry a lot, and I didn't know what to do.

After several months, my husband told me a few times that his parents wanted to talk to us. I didn't want to. I said I wanted to stay calm and not get stressed because I couldn't have my blood pressure rise. Besides, I had nothing to say to them.

Eli kept at it every day without letup. He said his parents were driving him crazy and that we had to go over.

"Then, just know that I'm afraid something will happen to the baby," I told him. Still, I gave in and went to the meeting, though I knew all too well what it would lead to.

With heavy hearts, we went over to his parents' house. I found myself sitting at a table where some sort of police-like interrogations were going on. The meeting began with criticism and comments about how I didn't wash the dishes and wasn't respectful enough.

My husband didn't say a thing. He just nodded his head in agreement. My hands began to tremble. I felt dizzy. I hadn't expected this, and I didn't dream that my husband of all people, the man who was supposed to protect me, wasn't on my side.

I'd never felt that bad in my life. When we got home, I told Eli how disappointed I was.

"I expected you to defend me. Even if I'm not so right, at least in front of your parents, show me that you support me."

Two days after that meeting, I went for a routine checkup, and suddenly they found something wrong.

I won't go into detail. Let me just say that after a month of tests and fears, I lost the baby. It happened in the hospital in a painful process.

Afterward, I was transferred back to the ward, where I fell asleep. My mother sat next to me all night, stroking my hands, sharing my pain.

A week went by. There was no one to comfort me for my loss. Except for the one time when my firstborn was brought to visit, I felt lonely and miserable, forlorn and forgotten.

When I was released from the hospital, I looked at the passing people, the women leaving with their babies, loaded with presents and balloons, surrounded by hugs and love. It was only I who sat there alone in the lobby, waiting, and no one even came to take me home.

The first few weeks, I was in terrible pain. I felt my world was destroyed. I was so lonely. All the joy of life was gone. I would take my son out to the park, and friends would say, "Mazel tov!" and then, "Where's the baby?"

I would choke and feel dizzy. I wanted to run away. I tried to smile, but I just couldn't.

From a person full of happiness and energy, I became a person who felt everything was dark and black. Even my son sensed when I was sad. He would lay his head on my lap, and I would melt and cry.

◀   ◀   ◀

One day my mother-in-law called and invited us to have dinner with them. I told my husband that I didn't want to go because I needed peace and quiet, and I didn't have the strength to talk to people.

My mother-in-law got mad. "I'm fed up with her. She's a baby and petty. What's the big deal? She's invited, so let her come! I don't understand that wife of yours. I don't want to speak to her," and she hung up.

I was shocked. I'd just gone through a traumatic experience, and I needed time to recover, and here she comes and says I'm a baby? Doesn't she have any feelings?

I decided that I also didn't want to speak to a woman with no feelings or compassion for another. And that's when the connection broke. The separation was very good for me. Less so for my husband. But he understood my situation and was considerate.

My husband had to hear from his uncles that I was having mental health issues, which is why I was acting strangely. He would take our son and go there for Shabbos, and I would stay alone with my parents.

He would come back completely exhausted and barely speak to me, and I realized they had filled him with complaints against me.

Sometimes I was curious to know what they were saying about me. That was a big mistake because when I pressed him, he'd tell me, and that caused explosions between us so large that we wouldn't speak to each other for a whole week.

He asked me not to ask him anymore so that we could protect ourselves.

☙   ☙   ☙

A month after I lost the baby, my life changed even more.

My husband and I sat on the couch and talked about the only issue we had left: the relationship with my mother-in-law. Suddenly, everything turned black. I felt terrified. I felt that the Angel of Death was right there in the house, just waiting for a signal to take action.

My whole body trembled. I felt it was the end. I left the house right away and called my parents to come to get me immediately because something was going to happen to me. They sounded terrified. They didn't understand what was happening to me.

We walked around the city for hours with me holding my mother's hand and feeling that any minute, something bad was going to happen. I was walking fast, in a daze, crying that I didn't want anything bad to happen to me.

I don't know who was more scared, me or my parents. After several hours of wandering all over, I calmed down a little and asked Eli if I could stay over at my parents' house that night because I was afraid to come home.

He gave his consent, and that night I stayed with my parents.

When I woke up in the morning, I could hardly believe I was alive. As soon as I got up, I said Modeh Ani with more feeling than I'd ever had. I felt like every word was talking directly to me.

I calmed down and forgot about this incident until it happened again.

I was sitting with my family on a bench near the house when suddenly it came upon me: wild fear, feeling like I couldn't breathe, my whole body shaking. I jumped up in a panic and started to pace, overcome by the dread that something bad was about to happen. My parents were frantic and didn't understand why it was happening again.

They took me to their family physician, who sent me for a few tests, including an EKG. The test results were good. So what was it?

The doctor called it a panic attack. She explained that the body can think there's real danger when there isn't. She recommended pills, but I refused. Why did I suddenly need pills? I was young and could handle the situation without medication. It would pass, and everything would be fine. Those were my thoughts.

But I guess I didn't know what I was up against. The attacks kept coming. I'd go to the emergency room with physical aches and pains or feeling my heart beating fast, take some tests, and be sent home.

Finally, I gave in and started taking pills. I realized that my family was getting worn down, too.

One day it dawned on me that people must think I'm crazy. At first, I felt ashamed. I was so young—too young to be taking tranquilizers. But I gradually realized I needed them because I couldn't handle it on my own.

I reminded myself that just as physical illness needs medical attention, so does mental illness, and there's nothing to be ashamed of getting whatever help you need.

I lived with it and tried to feel good about myself. I tried to hide my anxiety and the pills as much as possible.

I went to a psychologist at four hundred fifty shekels a session. It helped but didn't solve the problem.

At that time, my mother-in-law bought us an apartment.

Yes, you heard right. She looked for and found an apartment without us knowing anything about it. She signed the contract without us, too. When we were given the contract, I noticed that the apartment was registered in her name.

"Why aren't we listed on the contract?" I said to my husband. "Some of the money is ours."

"You're right. It's strange." He was just as surprised as I was and said he'd ask his mother about it.

"Why in the world would I have the apartment registered in your names?" she said without blinking an eye. "What if your wife decides tomorrow that she wants to divorce you? Why would she get half the apartment?"

I was shocked by the answer. "Is that what she wants?" I said to my husband. "For us to get divorced? People tend to say what's on their mind."

I felt I couldn't take any more. She was playing with our lives.

I told my therapist. I asked her how I could minimize the emotional damage to me from all these interactions with my mother-in-law.

"I'm sure you'll find the right way for you to handle it," she said.

When I came home, I told my husband, "Listen, now I know it's either her or me. Think it over and decide. I don't want to say anything about her. She may be a good mother but as a mother-in-law.... Please, ask a Rav, whoever you want. I need to cut off all contact with your family if I want to survive."

My husband started crying. I knew it was the cry of a suffering man who was torn between love for his parents and love for his wife. He started to say that he would never give me up, but I told him I didn't want an answer right then, only in a week.

Several days passed, and to be honest, I almost regretted putting him in such a tough spot. I was terrified he'd choose his parents. *Why am I putting him to such a difficult test?* I asked myself. *On one side, there's a wife with emotional problems, and on the other side is a home filled with everything you possibly could want. Why should he choose you?*

But five days later he asked to speak to me. He said he'd consulted with rabbis, and they all told him that he should take the terrible step to break away from his parents. They said that even if it was my fault, he should choose this step according to halachah. But they told him that, according to what he was saying, I was right. They said I had been living in an unbearable situation for years. They also explained to him that if he remarried, he'd have the same problem.

He told his parents about this consultation. His father was convinced, but his mother flew into a fit of rage. She shouted at him and accused him of being a *ben sorer u'moreh* and an ingrate. The conversation exploded.

The turnaround came from an unexpected direction.

His parents went to talk to Chacham Shalom Cohen, *shlita.* His mother wrote a long letter listing all her complaints. Chacham Shalom said he would talk to her son, my husband.

My husband went to him (I didn't know a thing about any of this), knowing that this was it. The Rav would tell him to honor his parents, and that would be the end of his marriage.

But Chacham Cohen is as wise as his title suggests, and what he said took my husband by surprise.

"I read your mother's claims. Normally a *dayan* must hear both sides, so I should have heard from your wife as well. But this time I don't need to because your mother's letter already convinced me that your wife is right. The letter was full of complaints and baseless hatred against your wife. There was not a single allegation that her daughter-in-law was disrespectful toward her or didn't obey her, only aspersions on her character, her taste in clothes, the way she takes care of the children, and the cleanliness of the home. It's not the mother-in-law's role to interfere in any of these things. Your mother convinced me that the best thing to do now would be to stay away temporarily."

"Temporarily." That's the word he used. But my husband knew what he had to do.

He told his parents we would be breaking off contact with them "temporarily" for the next six months.

What they didn't do! At first, they said, "Fine with us. If you don't want to have contact with us, don't." A few months later, they began sending people to patch things up. When that didn't turn out so well, they threatened and then begged. Then came more threats. But my husband didn't budge an inch from the instructions he'd been given by the Rav.

The six months turned into five years during which there was no contact, neither with his parents nor his siblings.

He may have lost them—temporarily—but he gained a healthy wife. I put all my energies into our marriage. I showed him great respect and repaid him for what he'd given up for me.

After five years, the relationship with my in-laws gradually began to return. At first, the meetings were stiff and formal. Then we came for Shabbos, and eventually, the relationship returned to regular daily contact.

This relationship is conducted under clear conditions: my

husband speaks with them only in my presence, and they don't criticize me in any way, even indirectly.

Initially, he refused to accept money from them. This was a sensitive point because most of the control started because of money. We were afraid to become financially dependent again.

Then, when I felt my pressure levels going down and felt less stressed, he "agreed" to accept support, too.

Meanwhile, more children were born to us, and the bond between me and my husband became exceptionally strong. We felt happier and more relaxed together. The panic attacks almost completely disappeared. I'm a much happier woman. Our home is full of love, humor, and music. My children grew up almost without feeling those five years (the disconnect was while the two older ones were young).

I can say I faced a well-known problem, but to a degree so extreme it could have destroyed our home. That we managed to safely escape it only made us stronger as a couple and as a family.

I'll end with a very simple message: Don't let anyone ruin your lives! Focus on your life together and keep going. If someone is plotting against you, just walk away. Disconnect from the bad even if there's some good on its side.

Deep inside, I'm so grateful to my husband for choosing me. I look back at that time and realize it wasn't an easy decision. Sometimes I'm surprised that he chose me again at that time when I was so depressed and full of anxiety.

When I say that to him, he tells me, "I didn't see what you had become. I saw who you'd always been. I knew this period was the result of mistreatment that wasn't your fault, but it was hard for me to admit it. I'm very happy I chose you. I chose you and got the person you were to begin with."

When Physics and Mysticism Meet...

The hero of this story is a physicist responsible for one of the most significant inventions in recent years in the field of defense.

The story zooms in on his early years, to look at what seems like an insurmountable obstacle blocking his path to professional success.

Apparently, though, there are Heavenly things that even physics can't explain.

My story is one of wondrous Divine Providence. It's a story that shows that nothing in the world happens by chance and that everything has an explanation even if we do not understand it at that moment.

We emigrated from Russia about twenty years ago.

After several years in Israel, my father managed to land a job that matched his skills as a construction engineer, while I was accepted into the Technion to study physics.

During my years of study, I drew close to the *chareidi*

community in Neve Shaanan, Haifa, which is not far from the Technion. Slowly but surely, I became more religious until, in the end, my wife and I and our children became fully *chareidi*.

Our children went to the local cheder and Bais Yaakov, and I became very close to the Rav of the neighborhood, who became a mentor to me and my family.

I completed my bachelor's degree in physics, followed by a master's degree with honors. After years of Sisyphean studies and enduring the financial hardship of supporting a family and paying for my studies, I entered the job market.

And here I encountered something strange.

Despite a profession in high demand, I just couldn't find a job.

I sent out applications to many companies in the north, but not a single one of them called me in for an interview.

The only responses I got were from companies located in Tel Aviv or further south.

The companies were solid, and the jobs were a good fit, but there was one problem: my family. My children's education. Our Rav. Our community. I couldn't see myself uprooting our whole family from this protective cocoon that was our whole world.

But months passed, and I wasn't bringing in any money.

With little choice, we began thinking of me taking a job in the central or southern region.

I went to several interviews. Each place offered me a job on the spot. All I had to do was pick the one I wanted.

I chose Orbotech, located in Yavne.

The reason was, again, the family and the children's education. Yavne is near Rehovot, and in Rehovot, I was told, there was a large Torah community where we would fit in.

With a heavy heart, I said goodbye to my friends and neighbors, and of course, my Rav, and we moved to Rehovot.
It was the week of *Parashas Chukas.*

I went to shul, where I was pretty well received. We davened Minchah and Kabbalas Shabbos, and then the rabbi spoke.

I was taken aback at hearing things I'd never thought I'd hear.

The rabbi spoke of how in the past, they didn't know how to identify a *parah adumah*, the red cow whose ashes were used for purification when the Beis Hamikdash stood, but now they do. How wonderful it was, he said, that nowadays we have scientific research so that now this whole thing about the red cow can be understood using the tools of science.

What in the world was he talking about? I'd been taught that if the Rishonim were like angels, we are human beings, and if they were like human beings, we are like donkeys. Who needed to listen to such nonsense, that in the past the Sages didn't understand what today we do understand?

I was devastated. It was a major crisis for me.

I couldn't understand why I'd been singled out for this punishment or why I'd been sent into exile. *Since I became a baal teshuvah,* I thought, *I've been doing everything for Hashem. I've educated my children in the best way, only for Him. Why is all this happening to me?*

Two weeks later, I received the news that my mother had cancer.

There were tests, results, and more tests. Then chemotherapy. Suddenly I had to spend a lot of time driving her back and forth to Tel Hashomer medical center. My father was getting on in years and was afraid of losing his job, so he wasn't very flexible. My bosses at Orbotech, on the other hand, said my hours could be flexible. Not only that, but I was the beneficiary of much goodwill from the CEO, who demonstrated exceptional understanding even though I was a new employee.

One day he came over to me and said he had a good friend in the medical field, and I should feel free to contact him for anything I needed. From that moment on, I had my own private Elimelech Firer: the CEO of Orbotech. He stood by our side through it all, accompanying us to the experts, finding the best doctors in the field, and even stepping in when a nurse failed to treat my mother with the proper respect.

It took me a while to see it, but I had my answer to "why is all this happening to me?" Without the move, I'd never have met the CEO of Orbotech, our guardian angel.

Hashem prepared the cure before the blow. He and only He had prevented me from finding a job up north and instead literally forced me to move down south where I would meet the right people to help my mother through her illness.

Three years later, my mother passed away.

She knew, as did we, that we'd done everything possible to prolong her life and enhance its quality. In fact, the cancer she had was a very aggressive type. Chances are she would have been given only several weeks to live. But I and the CEO of Orbotech were there for her every step of the way, which I'm certain added years to her life and helped her undergo treatments in the best way possible.

Then she passed away, and I sat shivah with my father in Kedumim.

I kept my phone on, both to direct people to where I was sitting shivah and to accept condolences from those who couldn't (or were too afraid to) go to Kedumim, a town in Samaria about an hour's drive east of Netanya.

On the second day of the shivah, I received three phone calls that can only be termed "totally unexpected."

They were from three of the leading companies in the field in which I work, all in the northern region. Each one called me with a similar message: "You sent us your résumé three years ago. We're getting back to you now."

Anyone familiar with the field knows this is something highly unlikely. If they don't get back to you within two weeks, you'll never hear from them again. And if they haven't called you in three years, they're not going to hire you even if you camp outside their office door.

For three of the leading companies in my field to get back to me on the same day, three years after I contacted them— right after I lost my mother and was actually able to go back up north—well, the only word I have for it is a miracle.

I explained to each of the callers that I was sitting shivah, but that as soon as it was over, I'd come for an interview.

And that's what I did. As soon as I got up from shivah, I set up the interviews. All three accepted me on the spot. All I had to do was find out which company offered the best terms.

Within a month, I'd returned to my community, to my Rav, to the shul, and to my children's educational institutions. I began work at Elbit, close to home, and on a higher pay scale than what my last job paid.

Guess what *parashah* it was when I returned?

Chukas.

I spoke in the shul. I told everyone my amazing story. I said the way it unfolded itself testifies like a thousand witnesses that what the speaker in that shul said was wrong. We can never fully comprehend Hashem's masterplan. No human being, no matter how brilliant or knowledgeable, can fathom the ways of Divine Providence. And any attempts to explain *chukas haTorah* using tools of logic is doomed to failure. When I felt that Hashem was "hiding His Face" from me by preventing me from finding a job near my community, could anyone know His plans? Could anyone know that three years later I would be in closer proximity to care for my mother during her illness? Could anyone have foreseen my relationship with the CEO of Orbotech, a person who could help more than anyone else? And how it was possible that only one day after this mission ended with my mother's passing suddenly the gates of Heaven opened in an astonishing manner when out of the blue I received three job offers that enabled me to move my family back to where we'd lived before, rejoining our community as if we'd never left.

When I'd finished speaking, the Rav stood up and said, "You may not have noticed, but your story closes a circle.

"You told us how hard it was for you to listen to that speaker in Rehovot who tried to say that the *gedolei olam* acted out of ignorance, and today we are supposedly smarter and can explain things using reason, so to speak.

"The *parah adumah* is enigmatic because it purifies the impure yet defiles the pure. But there is another enigma connected to it: the story of Damah ben Nesinah. Damah honored his father in an exceptional manner by giving up the fortune he could have made by selling a precious gemstone that lay under his sleeping father's pillow.

"In the merit of his exemplary *kibbud av*, a red cow was born in his herd. The rare cow's worth was equal to what he'd given up by not waking his father to make the sale.

"The birth of the red cow was not an act of logic but occurred by a Divine decree. And that's exactly what happened to you," he said. "You respected your parents. You gave your all for your mother's health, to care for her over the course of her illness, and you also honored your father, because thanks to you he was able to keep his job. Had he been absent from work two or three times a week at the age of seventy, they wouldn't have kept him on.

"You took it all on yourself, and the Creator of the world blessed you with a good job at an even higher salary than before, just as Damah ben Nesinah was rewarded with a red cow that brought him extraordinary wealth for no apparent reason."

I hope this story will inspire your readers, too, and deepen their trust in Hashem and His Divine Providence.

Even when it seems to us that Hashem is hiding His Face, we need to remind ourselves that it's only an illusion. Actually, He's still right there arranging our lives in the best possible way. There is a good reason for everything that happens, and only He knows that everything—but everything!—is to our benefit.

Surprise Rebellion

When a student declares a rebellion, it's good enough reason to take punitive action against her.
But what if that girl is the best girl in her class, both academically and in middos?
One thing is for sure: It's going to be a real story.

M y story spans thirty-five years, and I decided to tell it now for two reasons. One is that it comes to mind every year at high school registration time, and *every* year I promise myself I'm going to send it to you.

The second reason is that I saw a photo of the tombstone of your late son, Meir Zvi, and I was very moved by one line in particular.

Here's what happened…

I was a regular Bais Yaakov girl in one of the large *chareidi* population centers.

We were thirty girls in our class, a mix of unique individuals, each one different from the next. Just like today, we had girls who were very popular and some who weren't. There were the quiet girls and the louder ones, the hard workers and the ones who didn't put in that much effort.

But one girl stood out as being different from everyone else, one unforgettable girl. I know I'll never forget her, and I'm certain many others feel the same way. In fact, I think she's memorable to anyone who ever met her.

When I try to put into words what made her stand out, what comes to mind first is that she was a girl of sharp contrasts.

For instance, she was very low-key, but her opinion carried weight. Once she'd spoken, no one, and I mean no one, disagreed with her—not even in their thoughts. She was the leader, period.

The word leader usually has bad connotations. People think a girl who's a leader is condescending and looks down on other girls.

But not her.

Her name was Bracha. She was soft-spoken and self-effacing. She rarely talked and didn't stand out. It wasn't important to her to express her opinion, no matter what the topic of conversation.

She gave her opinion only when asked, and even then, only if she actually had an opinion on the issue under discussion. If she didn't have an opinion, she'd say, "I don't know what's right in this situation. You tell me."

She worked hard in school, but she never bragged about her marks. In fact, she'd hide her report card just like the weakest students in the class. If we hadn't known she was the top girl in the class academically, we could have mistakenly thought she had something to hide.

Bracha was tall and pretty, but we weren't jealous, partly because she tried hard to downplay it. She dressed in simple outfits anyone could afford and always looked put-together. She never looked sloppy, but she didn't look "perfect," either. That's who she was.

☙   ☙   ☙

We had a class committee, and at the start of every year, there were elections. I can't remember a single time when Bracha wasn't chosen to be on the committee. I can't even remember a time when she wasn't head of the committee. It was always Bracha and three other girls.

Then, in sixth grade, Bracha did something that got everyone upset.

Our class decided to have some fun by playing hooky for a couple of hours. We were just kids, and we weren't thinking too hard. As you can imagine, the adults were very unhappy about what we'd done. Our class was punished by being denied recess for the following two weeks plus a few other smaller penalties.

Two days later, Bracha submitted her resignation from the class committee.

Were we surprised! We hadn't thought resigning from the committee was even an option.

Her parents had spoken to her about her participation in the class's misbehavior. They said that as a leader, head of the class committee, she bore greater responsibility than the other girls. They told her to think about it and decide what she should do to pay the price for that responsibility.

The next day she wrote a letter of resignation, and that was the last time she agreed to head the class committee.

I remember her resignation made waves not only in our class but throughout the whole school. Interestingly, it didn't damage her standing in the least. If anything, it added a certain glow to her already shining image. She became a role model for all the girls in school.

Life continued, and before we knew it, we were in eighth grade.

The next step was high school.

The application process started in the middle of the year. Even back then, there was a lot of stress over who would be accepted and who wouldn't—and everyone knew that some of the considerations that could tip the scale were trivial.

Just like today, back then we'd hear about girls who didn't get accepted though they deserved to. People tried using pull. Sometimes it worked and sometimes it didn't. Everyone knew if you had a sister who went to the school, you had a better chance. These are terrible things that existed back then and continue today. If you ask me, things have only gotten worse, maybe because the *chareidi* population has grown or because the competition between schools is more intense.

The ones to pay the price were the girls without connections or money, or, worst of all, the girls who weren't of the "right" ethnic origin.

(Who knows how many boys and girls are devastated each year by this flawed system! Not that I'm saying schools have to accept every girl who applies. But I do think the admittance criteria shouldn't be based on social class and definitely not on ethnic origin. It just shouldn't be that way.)

The girls in our class were as nervous about getting into the high school of their choice as everyone else. Though I was born into the "right" ethnic group as far as the system was concerned, I was still nervous. My fears were foolish, though, because within a short time, I received a letter embossed with the school logo from the high school I'd listed as my first choice, bearing the message, "We are pleased to inform you..."

Most of the girls in my class got the same letter. Then we discovered a painful reality: three girls from our class weren't accepted to the high school of their choice.

One of the three had average grades, the second was a top student, and the third was both smart and had beautiful *middos*, but came from a simple family that wasn't Ashkenazi.

How did we feel? Exactly the way eighth graders today feel when something like this happens.

There were excited cries of joy about being accepted—and some sad faces of those who were rejected. There was caring—and indifference. There were attempts to help—and comments like, "Well, excuse me, but there are other schools, and they don't have to take *everyone*."

The girl who was an average student found a different school, and she seemed happy. But the other two girls were devastated. Their grief cast a deep shadow on our class, but we, like them, knew there was nothing we could do about it.

At least, that's what we thought.

One day, when it seemed like everyone had accepted the decree (except for the two girls who still didn't have a high school), Bracha walked into our classroom and signaled she had something to say.

We all fell silent.

If the girl we looked up to the most wanted to tell us something, we were going to listen. Besides, it was so out of character for her. She'd never been the dramatic type.

"I hereby announce that as long as two girls (she said their names) aren't accepted to the school, I'm not going there either. And I think if other girls join me, it will help them get in."

Once the words were spoken, there was no taking them back. None of us will ever forget that moment—neither the words nor the person who said them. The expression on her face was a mixture of nobility, rage, gentle determination, pain, and relief. She was obviously speaking from a very deep place inside herself. We knew she meant what she said, and she'd do it, no matter what.

We sat there in stunned silence.

A girl stood up and walked over to stand next to Bracha. "I'm with you," she said.

Another two girls joined them, and then another girl stood up and walked over to the group.

Five girls. It was no longer a protest; it was the beginning of a rebellion.

I wasn't one of the five.

It was as if someone had thrown a hand grenade. We knew it was only a matter of time before it exploded.

But it didn't explode.

The school ignored this declaration of rebellion, either because they thought that was the correct response or because they were too shocked.

The next day, ten more girls joined the rebellion, and on the third day, almost the whole class, me included, joined. The protest could no longer be stopped.

Bracha was sent home from school. I remember watching her as she obediently took her things and left. She did it without any chutzpah but holding her head high.

The school was sure this would break the rebellion, but it

didn't work out that way. Teachers talked to us girls, but we stood strong and declared that if the two girls were not accepted, we wouldn't go to that high school, either.

Now there was a real commotion. Furious phone calls were made telling the girls that what they were doing was wrong and threatening repercussions. The girls stayed united. I don't know where we got the strength. The adults might have thought it was peer pressure, but it wasn't, because no one pressured the two girls who refused to take part in the protest. There was energy in the air and a sense of big changes taking place.

The parents were divided. Some insisted their daughters not take part in the protest, while others actually encouraged them in it. A lot of pressure was put on Bracha's parents to get them to change her decision. Everyone knew that once she changed, all the other girls would follow her lead. But Bracha's parents said they supported her fully, just as they had supported her decision to resign from the class committee when she didn't try to stop her classmates' from pulling a foolish but chutzpadik prank. They said that if they were given a good reason why these excellent girls weren't accepted, maybe they'd reconsider.

But no such reason was forthcoming.

Only after the end of the school year did the saga end. The high school gave in. They accepted the girls who'd been discriminated against, and we began high school on a high note, more of a close-knit group than ever. If the school worried (with justification) that this unity would cause chutzpah and misbehavior, they soon found out that the opposite was true. Bracha stayed the same quiet, gracious leader, and she took it in the best possible direction. Every single girl in the class without exception was refined, acted and dressed with *tznius*, and was respectful of parents and teachers. Over the years, our class earned distinction for following school directives and guidelines.

One by one, we all married *bnei Torah* and built wonderful homes.

It came as no surprise to anyone that Bracha chose to become a teacher. In her own quiet way, with her inherent grace and determination, she became a revered teacher who inspired her students to follow the same path of *yiras Shamayim*, humility, modesty, nobility, and strength.

About twelve years ago, Bracha was stricken with cancer. All of *Klal Yisrael* prayed for her recovery, but six months later, she was no longer with us. She left a grieving husband and eight children.

I attended her funeral and was not at all surprised to see every single one of our classmates there.

We all stood there at the funeral as prominent rabbis eulogized her, but our thoughts turned inward.

Sounds of sobbing interspersed with the eulogies. We classmates mourned the passing of this righteous woman. We all knew who she was and what a revolution she'd made.

The two girls who owed their lives to Bracha cried hardest. She was willing to stand up for their rights even at the cost of great personal sacrifice. She'd led the battle for justice and equality and won.

Two weeks ago, Rabbi Walder, I saw a picture of your son's headstone, on which is engraved: "Beloved son, exemplary husband, and devoted father who gave his all to family, friends, and humanity. A man of truth and righteousness, a fighter for justice, virtuous and noble, beloved by all."

Right away, I thought of Bracha, *a"h*, and her fight for justice, and I realized that Hashem gathers to Him all those people. He wants them by His side. Probably from there, they make an even stronger impact on our world.

In the Shadow of Revenge

*For many years, a child who became a youth and
then a man carried within him the searing pain of a
longstanding hurt done to him by a classmate.*
An uncontrollable desire for revenge burned.
But this time, the revenge was fatal.
Is there a way to go back?

It all began twenty-six years ago when I was twelve and a
half. I attended an excellent Talmud Torah affiliated with a
certain community. There was just one problem: my family
didn't belong to that community.

At first, it wasn't a problem. No one cared where I came
from though staff and pupils alike knew I wasn't part of their
kehillah. The problem started when I entered sixth grade. An
argument arose between the community I belong to and the
one my school was part of. Soon we kids knew everything that
was going on, and in no time at all, someone pounced on the

fact that in their very school, there was a kid who belonged to the enemy camp.

The first attacks were general ones, against my *kehillah* and its leaders (I'm not going to give away or even hint at any identifying details). Then they became more personal.

Despite the many years that have passed since then, I remember vividly every detail of my suffering back then. They mocked me personally, laughed out loud, humiliated me, mimicked me, tattled on me to teachers, and made sure I got more than my fair share of punishments.

The teachers blamed me for the whole problem. They told my parents about everything that happened in such a way as to make them think I was the one provoking everyone. My father had many talks with me, all of them about how I had to stop taunting my friends. I tried telling him what was really going on, but I could see he didn't believe me.

I can sort of understand why he didn't believe me. The suffering at school made me very tense and irritable, and I had angry outbursts at home. My siblings and my mother suffered the most. I was still afraid of my father, but the others bore the brunt of my rages.

My parents took me to a psychologist (not all that common or accepted back then) and told him I had a problem both at school and at home. They had no idea that what was happening at home was caused by what was happening in school.

I went from therapist to therapist while the bullying went from bad to worse. At school, I was being hit both by kids and staff. As if that wasn't enough, I got it at home too. Except that at home, I hit back—a lot.

My parents were desperate. They didn't know what to do with me.

I got to one therapist who had a big influence on me. He

taught me how to ignore provocations, how to calm down and not explode.

There was a short period of calm. But then the leader of the pack of bullies (let's call him Meir) didn't like the fact that my behavior improved and that I was even earning some occasional words of praise from teachers. He turned to mean, painful ways of provoking me. When I held myself back from responding and remained in control, it just made him try harder.

He'd put me down all the time, but I said nothing. He'd pull the chair out from under me just as I was about to sit on it. I'd fall down, everyone would laugh, and still I wouldn't react.

In the dining room, he'd take away my plate, and I'd just go and take another one. He'd push me, and I'd fall flat on my face, but I wouldn't say a thing.

It was abuse, plain and simple.

Inside, I was broken. Depressed. My therapist decided I should switch to a school in a different country. In other words, he gave up, too.

As we were trying to decide if my going to a school abroad was a good idea or not, Meir solved the problem. One day he opened a hose full blast on me and soaked me from top to bottom while the other kids stood there laughing.

When I went back into the classroom, I was thrown out by the teacher—yes, you heard right—who shouted at me for daring to open the water to entertain the other kids.

I tried to explain that I was the victim here. I suggested he ask the other kids in the class, which he did. They said, "He (meaning me) opened it."

When I got home, I told my father I was ready to transfer to a school abroad. Inside, I had a few other thoughts as well. I wanted to shout to the whole world and tell them what was going on. Let everyone know what that mean, nasty kid had done to me.

This took place a month before Meir's bar mitzvah. My parents bought tickets for a flight leaving in three weeks. That way I'd at least be spared the humiliation of not being invited to his bar mitzvah.

I decided to write down everything Meir had done to me. I wrote and cried and then wrote some more. I didn't leave anything out. I titled it, "I Accuse."

I wrote down every single detail of his torments and bullying, and then I wrote what I thought about him as a person, his character, his terrible *middos*. I added my prediction of how he'd turn out, including pity for the poor girl who would marry him and how miserable his children would be if he were even blessed to have any.

I wrote furiously, with determination fueled by hatred.

And I had a plan that I felt was the right thing to do.

A week before the flight, I went to a photo store and made two hundred copies of my three-page letter. That's right, two hundred.

The only person I let in on the secret was my best friend, who hadn't gone to the same school but was part of my community. He knew the story and immediately agreed to my request.

I gave him the package of pages, and a few days later, I flew abroad.

He stayed behind with the pages and the job I'd given him: to pass them out at Meir's bar mitzvah celebration.

I was just a kid. I didn't think about what it would mean. As far as I was concerned, he was my biggest enemy who had destroyed my life. I wanted him to feel the same pain on his biggest day.

I arrived at my relatives' home in the United States. My parents were both from the States, so I spoke English. As an aside, I want to mention that lots of kids of new immigrants suffer socially because of the different mentalities.

I fit right in with my new school. I felt like I'd been released from slavery to freedom. There I was, in a new place, in a new community that fit me like a glove, with kids who welcomed me. Not like "Tzviki Green."

Sure, I missed my parents. But having friends and being part of a friendly group made it easy for me to overcome other difficulties.

After a couple of days, I remembered the mission I'd given my friend. I decided it was a bit too much to distribute copies of my letter at Meir's bar mitzvah party. Maybe he should give them out later. Due to the time difference, though, I didn't manage to get in touch with my friend. It was two days after the bar mitzvah when I finally reached him and asked him if he'd given out my letter.

He said yes.

I felt really bad, but I didn't say anything to him. After all, I was the one who'd asked him to do it. I couldn't come to him now with any complaints. I thanked him and hung up. I felt like my revenge was too cruel. I realized I'd probably ruined Meir's bar mitzvah celebration, destroyed his happiness on that day. He'd deserved to be punished, but that was taking things too far.

I stayed in the States for a year, and then I went back to Israel. While I'd been away, my parents had moved to another city. Since then, they've moved twice to other cities, and maybe that's symptomatic of the exiles new immigrants go through.

Meanwhile, I entered a yeshivah that suited me to a T. It had no connection with the elementary school I'd attended because it was a different community altogether. The suffering I'd gone through was very helpful to me because it toughened me, and I started to soar in my learning and socially as well.

Every so often, I'd remember that deed, and each time I'd regret it anew. I was mature enough to realize that what I'd done was really bad. Even if Meir had acted badly toward me, there are certain things you just don't do, and destroying someone's bar mitzvah is one of them. Feelings of regret plagued me for years.

By the time I entered *shidduchim*, I was considered a good catch. I got engaged to a top girl, and a date was set for the wedding.

The search for a wedding hall took me back in time. It brought to mind Meir's bar mitzvah and the shame he must have experienced. I knew a *chassan* is forgiven all his sins. Still, I had a feeling I wouldn't be forgiven for this sin, the same way Yom Kippur doesn't atone for things between one person and another.

I was no longer the child I'd once been. I was a serious, mature *bachur*, sensitive and considerate of others. The story disturbed me and gave me no peace. The closer we got to my wedding day, the more strongly I felt I had to go to Meir and ask his forgiveness.

Once I decided to do this, I wasted no time in trying to locate him. I contacted a former classmate whose phone number I still had and asked him where Meir was learning. I was afraid he'd ask me what I wanted from Meir after what I'd done to him. Happily, he didn't ask and just told me the name of the yeshivah.

It was a week before my wedding. I went to Meir's yeshivah, quaking with fear. I didn't know how he'd react, how he'd be able to forgive the person who'd ruined his bar mitzvah. It took a lot of courage to approach him. I knew he might turn his back on me.

I asked someone to go inside and call him.

An unfamiliar bearded fellow came out of the building and walked over to me.

"Are you Meir?" I asked.

He said yes and added his family name.

I told him my name.

"The one who was in my class?" he asked.

"Yes," I said.

"I didn't recognize you."

An awkward silence.

"What do you want?" he finally said.

"I'm getting married in a week, and I wanted to ask you *mechilah*."

"*You* want to ask *me*?!" he said in obvious shock. "It seems to me I'm the one who should be asking you for *mechilah*. You left the school because of that story with the water."

"Yes, but what happened with your bar mitzvah—"

"That you didn't come? I think you were already in America by then."

I was confused. The thought flashed through my mind to tell Meir about the letter, but I decided to be cautious. "Still, I'd like to ask you to forgive me if I caused you any anguish."

"I'm the one who has to ask you for forgiveness," he said. "I caused you a lot of agony. I was young and stupid. I didn't think about what I was doing. I really want to ask you to forgive me. I think you left the school and the country because of me. I had a lot of regrets about that. I'm the one who should have come to you. I don't think you need to ask me. You did nothing but suffer from me."

I told him I forgave him, and we parted as friends, with me handing him an invitation to my wedding.

Boy, was I confused. I didn't know what to think. No way could he forget something as bad as what I'd done.

I had to find out what really happened

I paid a visit to my old friend, the one I left the copies with.

It was Friday night. At the yeshivah, they told me he was home, so that's where I went.

We greeted each other and exchanged pleasantries for a few minutes, and then I asked him, "Tell me something. Do you remember I gave you a couple of hundred copies of a letter to give out at Meir's bar mitzvah?"

"Uh...yeah. Sure I remember."

"So tell me about it. How did you give them out?"

"Uh...well..." He gave a small cough. "I went there with a plan of how to give them out, but when I walked in, all the kids were so happy, and I saw his father and uncles, and it suddenly struck me that it wasn't so simple. Maybe you don't know, but I hated him for what he did to you. But thoughts are one thing, and actions are another. I didn't have the heart to destroy all the *simchah*, so I left and went home. And then, a few days later, you called. I didn't know what to say, but I remembered that it's okay to fudge a little for the sake of peace. So I told you I'd left the letters. That way, it was only half untrue, because I really did leave them somewhere."

"Where did you put them?" I asked. Now I was afraid the papers had gotten into the wrong hands.

"Down in our storage room," he said. "I'll show you."

He led me down a flight of stairs to the storage room, opened the metal door, and switched on the light. Then he began plowing through boxes and furniture no one would ever use again, but that just couldn't be thrown out. In a carton underneath a pile of books, he found the letters I'd photocopied. Some were blurred from water damage, but you couldn't miss the title: "I Accuse."

"Do you forgive me?" he asked.

"Of course I forgive you for not giving them out," I told him. "If you had, in Heaven, neither of us would have been forgiven."

I couldn't stop my tears. I felt a boulder roll off my heart. I gave my startled friend a bear hug and said, "You saved my life. Now I can get married with a full heart."

That's the story, and I don't think I need to point out the moral. People get angry at times and want to take revenge, but they don't always know where to draw the line. My anger was stronger than my compassion, but, fortunately, my friend couldn't bring himself to snuff out someone's joyous moment.

I went to my wedding like an angel, and I felt like one, too— white, free of sin. I thought of all the challenges I'd faced and all the suffering that had surely erased my transgressions. My joy was total, knowing I didn't have an ugly stain on my conscience.

Meir, dressed differently than all my other friends, appeared toward the end of the wedding. Not a single person there knew who he was or what he was to me—or why I hugged him and pulled him into an exuberant dance.

I think Meir was even more clueless than the rest. To him, I was a figure from the past, a boy he'd bullied. He didn't know that my happiness stemmed from the deed that hadn't stained my conscience.

It was really the joyous voice of a *chassan* at his chuppah—knowing that a foolish act in his youth could have cast a shadow on his moments of supreme joy.

Let There Be Love, Friendship, and Peace

The main benefit of family is the love and togeth-erness, being there for each other.

But there are families where each individual is alone in the group, and instead of togetherness, there is jealousy, competition, and hatred.

This is the story of a family whose children excelled in all areas–especially sibling rivalry taken to an extreme.

Is there any way to break the cycle?

I'm the mother of seven successful, healthy children. Every single one of them without exception is considered outstanding. Each has brought us a lot of *nachas* and honor in almost *every* area. And when I say almost, I mean except for one area.

The relationship between them.

It's always been bad, and when I say bad, I mean worse than you can imagine.

I'm not talking about normal sibling rivalry. I'm talking about outright hatred.

It took a while before my husband and I were forced to admit we had a serious problem on our hands.

What took us so long? We were blinded by all the good things going on. Besides, sibling rivalry is common, especially when children are young. But when our eldest turned nineteen and the youngest was five, it dawned on us that while our children had grown up, their behavior hadn't grown up with them.

We'd done a good job of getting them all interested in their studies. We'd gotten them excited about working hard and achieving academic excellence. And we'd helped them develop their social skills so they were very popular kids as well. Our failure to create a sense of unity among them stood in stark contrast. It might be that our emphasis on achievement is what led to the strong competition between them that turned into jealousy and hatred.

Imagine a home where the best possible reality is that two brothers don't talk to each other. That was much better than what usually went on—the insults, criticism, snide remarks, and aggressive behavior.

A child would rather throw his game on the floor than let his brother play with it, or forgo a trip if that would prevent his siblings from going on one, too.

It didn't end at home, either. The enmity and animosity came out in school, as well. When a child was hurt by a friend, his big brother was happy about it—and he let his friends know it. Their classmates caught on fast to what was going on between the brothers. Because the brothers were popular, their friends tried to prove their loyalty by hurting the other brother as much as possible. We had no idea this was going on until the teachers drew our attention to the fact that something very unhealthy was happening in school.

I remember a period when my husband and I told the children that any instance of such behavior would be punished severely. The guilty party would have his favorite possessions confiscated, and other privileges and perks would be taken away. The threat worked, or at least it looked like the kids reduced the amount of hatred between then, but it was like offering a Band-Aid for heart disease. The visibility of the problem diminished, but the problem itself wasn't solved and grew worse from day to day.

We would look at other families and see how love and camaraderie prevailed among all the siblings. We'd see brothers and sisters helping each other, cheering each other on, and protecting each other. We pointed this out to our children, but the response we got was a mix of cynicism and disdain. They saw such behavior as a sign of weakness and stupidity. They told us what poor students those children were and how unpopular. It was as if they'd established their own "religion" in which every manifestation of loyalty, love, and friendship is a form of weakness. I'm ashamed to say it, but these are the kids we raised, and that was their behavior.

When one of the children threatened his older brother that he'd ruin his *shidduchim,* we realized things couldn't go on this way.

Meanwhile, our eldest got engaged and married. A year later, his sister married.

Throughout the engagements and weddings, the children somehow maintained a "family" look. Actually, the distance and hatred remained, and the bride and groom who entered our family picked up on the situation even during the engagement period. You'd have to be stupid to miss it.

The bride took sides quickly. Our eldest must have told her

in detail the shortcomings of each sibling, and she fully sided with him. I think part of her reason for so closely aligning with him was because he has a strong, powerful personality. She had no chance of standing up to him, not in this matter or in any other.

🖅   🖅   🖅

The daughter who got married next took an unusual step. She cut off all contact with our family.

We didn't notice it at first. But when she didn't visit for over for six months, we asked her about it. She was evasive and said it didn't work out for them because they lived in another city, and it was hard for them to travel. That struck us as strange. She was a good girl, a girl who loved being at home. It wasn't like her to cut off all contact like that.

We began to suspect that our son-in-law was making her stay away. We'd heard about such things. My husband found an opportunity to speak with him, and he disclosed that the distancing was our daughter's idea, not his. He said she insisted he have nothing to do with her parents' home. He said that personally, he felt bad about it and encouraged her to keep in touch, but she refused to talk about it.

Naturally, we were very hurt. I went to see her and tried to raise the topic, but she didn't want to talk about it. When I persisted, she said, "Our house is like a madhouse. I don't know how I came out of it normal. Maybe because I didn't know things could be different. Once I got engaged and visited my husband's house, it was like another planet. There was a Shabbos table. I saw how much the kids loved each other, to the point of actual admiration. At first, I thought it was put on, a show for the guest. We used to put on an act when there were guests, too. Not to the extent of love, *chas v'shalom*, but at least we controlled ourselves and hid the hatred and swallowed the barbs.

"As time went on, though, I realized that this was a home where each of the siblings would give his life for the others. And I'm not exaggerating. I heard stories of a brother who got beaten up defending his brother from some toughs who attacked him. All that mattered to him was that his brother escape. I heard about a sister who helped her younger sister study though it meant she'd get a lower grade herself. I saw with my own eyes love and brotherhood between siblings. There were things that really amazed me, like a ten-year-old boy who showed me his nine-year-old sister's violin and boasted in front of everyone how much the violin was worth and how his sister knew to play better than any other girl in her school, city, country, or anywhere in the world. He begged his sister to play for me.

"She couldn't really play all that well, but it was the most beautiful music I'd ever heard. Seeing his eyes sparkle with pride at his sister's playing brought me to tears. What love he'd shown for his sister! What his pride in her success! I'd never seen anything like it. I didn't even know such a thing existed.

"Everything came to the surface there. All the insults and disparaging comments I'd gotten from my big brother, my little brother, everyone together... And that's when I began thinking about what the right thing was to do.

"After I got married, the picture came into sharper focus. I saw how my husband's brothers and sisters found ways to make each other happy whenever they could, giving them small gifts or making a party for them. I saw how they got together secretly to prepare a song for a brother or sister, and none of them opted out or acted like they were forced to join in. They did it because they wanted to express their love and encouragement. I saw before me a living example of what we learned in Yirmiyahu:

'Each one shall help his fellow, and to his brother, he shall say, "Strengthen yourself." I realized that the home I'd grown up in destroyed the people living in it. It was an emotionally toxic environment. I don't know how I survived."

She burst into tears, and I cried right along with her. I had nothing to say. She was right.

"Where did we go wrong?" I asked her through my tears.

She didn't take long to answer. "I respect you and Abba and I love you both, and I never wanted to think of you as being wrong. I chose to see only the good parts. You and Abba have given me so much. Whatever strengths I have are only from you. That overshadowed all the rest.

"I think you and Abba are the reason we weren't destroyed emotionally, because you weren't part of this game. You didn't attack us or hurt us. You didn't humiliate us or verbally abuse us. Instead, you empowered us to succeed and not be affected by it. I really love you both, and I know I owe you more than any child owes her parents. But I just can't go back there. I'm so sorry, Mommy. I need to stay far away from dangerous places, and that's what the house I grew up in is—a dangerous place."

Her words reverberated as I drove home. The fact that she had *middos* good enough to see the good in all this evil and not to blame us for the terrible situation enabled me to accept her criticism and realize that it was justified.

Now it was up to us as parents to change the situation.

At that time, our third child, a son, got engaged. The girl he chose was soft-spoken and kind. I expected that she'd be like my first daughter-in-law, that she'd go along with him and join forces against everyone in our family.

Surprise! Though quiet, she had her own mind. She caught

on fast to the family dynamics. She waited patiently until the wedding, and only then began expressing her opinion.

It was a while before she talked to me. First, she explained to her husband (my son) that his house looked perfect from the outside, but was really sick on the inside, that brothers and sisters couldn't behave that way to each other. She refused to say anything bad about any of his siblings and said it was crucial to their marriage that they both be on the same page about trying to fix things.

She was so respectful, he couldn't refuse. He saw that what she was saying was coming from a good place and not out of a desire for control.

And then she asked me if she could speak to me.

I was uncomfortable, but she got me to relax and spoke kindly. Like my daughter, she assured me that she wasn't blaming, but she felt we did have to make major changes to erase the hatred between the siblings and to become a normal family. These were her exact words: "To become a normal family."

I didn't deny what she'd said. I told her it was bothering me no end, and I asked her to help me change the situation.

"You don't expect me to be your mother-in-law," she said with a smile. "That's not happening. My suggestion would be to consult a professional about what to do."

"You're smart, and you've got a lot of insight. Do me this favor. Please."

Finally, she agreed. We brainstormed together, thinking about steps we could take to change the situation.

Our first decision was that we'd work on the four children still at home and not try to change the marrieds, especially since we didn't really have to change two of them.

She began by asking me a simple question: "Try to remember if you've ever tried anything that worked."

"Let me think," I said. "Yes, there was something that worked. We stopped their enmity in school by giving a significant punishment and threatening more if they continued."

"Well, then why don't we expand that to include the home?" she asked.

We put together a document, a kind of proclamation that informed our children that we do not allow any act of hostility or antagonism toward a sibling, whether verbal or physical. We didn't specify what we would do, but we wrote, "We will do everything we can, including contacting people outside the home to get involved."

The project was off and running. Whenever a child hurt his brother, he had to deal with phone calls from people he knew, from his teacher through the gabbai in shul all the way to the lecturer we'd invited to our home to talk about "*bein adam lechaveiro*."

Beyond that, we took significant steps: If a child teased his brother at school with what he said to a friend, he was kept home from school for a week. Each day he'd get a different phone call with a fiery lecture. The speeches weren't attacks or threats. They were soft-spoken, persuasive, and heartfelt, but their very existence was undoubtedly a great discomfort for the child or teen.

Change turned out to be easier than we'd thought. A month was all it took for all the hostility to end, both in public and in private. But we hadn't eliminated the negative emotions. You can deal with actions more readily than with feelings.

Three years ago, on the advice of this daughter-in-law, we

216

decided to travel on Erev Rosh Chodesh Sivan with our unmarried children to the tomb of the Shelah Hakadosh.

We got there and joined the large crowd streaming to the site. We went with the flow, heading for a place where we could pour out our hearts in prayer.

And then something happened that I can only call an open miracle.

Before we reached the area of the gravesite, where men and women go their separate ways, two men were walking in front of us: one tall and sturdy, the other disabled—his whole right side paralyzed, from head to foot.

They reached the curb, and the disabled man fell flat on his face.

He was slightly injured, and blood dripped down his face. As a nurse by profession, I pulled out the basic first aid equipment I always carried with me and treated his wounds.

We made sure he drank water, then led him to a nearby bench to rest. While he was resting, I asked the two men a few questions about who they were and where they came from.

They told me they were brothers. The injured man closed his eyes and said he needed to rest. His brother sat down beside him, and we moved a little away to give them space. Then a woman came over and said she was their mother. In a whisper, she told us their story.

"Until four years ago, my younger son, the one who just got hurt, was the most successful boy in the neighborhood. He was a smart, hardworking, and likable boy, number one in everything.

"His brother, the one sitting next to him, is a year older, and to tell the truth—" She paused as if wondering whether to say what she was about to. "He envied his younger brother. Envied him and hated him. Not that the older one was a *nebach* or anything. But he couldn't stand his younger brother's success. He did everything he could to annoy him and hurt him. My husband and I tried to put a stop to it, but nothing we did worked. The jealousy and hatred between them was too strong.

"Four years ago, my younger son was outside playing when he collapsed. He was rushed to the hospital. He'd had a stroke, which is very rare for someone his age. They saved his life, but he remained paralyzed on his right side.

"You're seeing him after a long rehabilitation process. His being able to walk is a miracle. We're dealing with a double catastrophe. Not only is he disabled, but he remembers the good days before it happened, and that makes him even more depressed.

"As soon as it happened, his brother's animosity disappeared. But it was replaced by strong feelings of guilt. He blames himself for what happened. He feels that his bad thoughts, jealousy, and impatience with his brother are what caused it. Nothing we said helped. We took him to *rabbeim*, who explained to him that everything is decreed by Hashem. But he couldn't be budged. 'You don't know what I thought about him.' he told them. 'What happened to him is exactly what I hoped would happen to him. I'm to blame.'

"So now we're taking care of one son who's physically handicapped and another who is broken mentally and tormented by guilt.

"The only good thing to come of this is that at least they now love each other. You won't find such devotion between brothers anywhere else in the world.

"But why did we have to go through something like this for the two boys to love the other?"

She thanked me profusely, gave a deep sigh, and walked over to where her sons sat waiting.

We stood there in silence. No one said a word. Everything that needed to be said had just been said by that woman, the mother of those boys. Only a miracle could have brought us to that very spot at that very moment so that we could hear their story.

One thing was certain. Not a single one of my children standing there with me—two sons and two daughters—wanted to go through a traumatic experience to stop hating each other.

Then we entered the *tziyun*, me and two daughters, my husband and two sons.

I took out the prayer of the Shelah Hakadosh that I say every year, but this time certain words leaped out at me. I'd never paid them special attention before:

"It is for this reason that I come to ask and plead before You that my children and grandchildren be upright offspring... Grant them health, honor, strength, and give them stature, beauty, charm, and kindness. May there be love, brotherhood, and peace among them."

I burst into tears and couldn't stop crying. I pointed to the words to show my daughters what had made me cry. Later I found out that my husband did the same with the boys.

It's been four years since that happened. I'm one of those who goes to the grave of the Shelah Hakadosh every year. Now I go not only to pray but also to give thanks for the good because everything's changed completely. From hatred to love, from weakness to strength, from alienation to connection, from contempt to caring, encouragement, and admiration.

So much has changed in our family. Now we're a family in

the true meaning of the word. Our oldest is coming along, more slowly than we'd like, but you can't compare it to what it used to be, and when there's no partner to fight with, there's no fight.

Thanks to my dear daughter-in-law, and especially because of the miracle that happened to us at the *kever* of the Shelah Hakadosh, we're now one big happy family among whose children there is love, brotherhood, and peace.

Anniversary Present

A young woman prepares an anniversary sur-
prise for her husband.
She remembers everything necessary for the sur-
prise down to the last detail.
She forgets only one thing.
The date.

I was born in New York and went to pre-1A, cheder, and
mesivta there. When I was nineteen, my parents, after
discussing it with a *gadol*, decided to send me to the Mir to
learn in Yerushalayim.

Thousands of boys study abroad in Brisk, the Mir, and other
places, but for me, the change was tough. They say all beginnings
are hard, and this beginning, without a single relative in Eretz
Yisrael, was extremely hard, particularly for an introvert like me.

In time, I made friends who, like me, had come from afar
to exile themselves to a place of Torah. I also made one close

friend, Danny, who was not only a *yerei Shamayim* but a tremendous *masmid* with a heart of gold.

Danny had come to the Mir three years before me, and he turned that first, most difficult time into the happiest and most elevated time that could be. He introduced me to hosts who were *talmidei chachamim* from the States, who invited me for Shabbos. He also arranged the best *chavrusos* for me.

On Shabbos, Danny arranged for us to learn together and used the time to review what we'd learned the previous week. Another of his virtues that impressed me was his truthfulness. He never lied, never "smoothed things out." The statement "Hashem's seal is truth" applied to him more than any other statement.

I decided I wanted to be just like him, and so I took it upon myself to stay far away from lies. Maybe it can't be considered as "taking it upon myself," because it's one of the 613 commandments: *Midvar sheker tirchak* (one must distance oneself from falsehood).

Five years later, I got engaged to an American girl who was spending a year in seminary in Yerushalayim.

I later learned that Danny had a hand in this, too. My father-in-law had come for a visit during *bein hazmanim* and met Danny in a *beis medrash* in Yerushalayim. He told Danny he was looking for a boy for his daughter, described the type of *bachur* he was looking for, and then added that he wanted "the crown jewel" of the *bachurim* in the yeshivah. Danny told him that there were a lot of diamonds, but if he was looking for a flawless, polished diamond, he knew just one, and he gave him my name. That's how I got engaged.

The wedding date was set for the third of Adar. My *kallah*

and I decided to have the wedding in the States because both our families live there. It sounds like a logical choice, but I didn't take into account the ramifications. A week later, when I started to picture "this is how my wedding will look," an image suddenly popped up in my mind, and I said to myself, *Wait a minute— how will all my friends from yeshivah participate?*

There was no way my Israeli friends could be there. But what about the *chutznikim?*

I quickly realized that the date we'd chosen would make it hard for people to attend.

If the wedding had been scheduled for the end of Adar, *bachurim* could leave a couple of weeks early for the Pesach break. Or, if it were set for the middle of the winter, friends probably would have come. But one month before the usual return home for Pesach was the least suitable time for a trip to the States for *bachurim* who would be going back anyway a month later. No one would leave yeshivah a month early, and no one would return to yeshivah for just three weeks.

The venue was near where my in-laws live, a six-and-a-half-hour drive from New York. The drive from my parents' home to the wedding hall takes longer than that, which meant that, most likely, even my childhood friends wouldn't make it.

When I realized all this, I got very down. What kind of wedding would I have? Who would dance for me? Who would rejoice with me?

Three weeks before the wedding, on the day I flew home, I said goodbye to Danny. I had tears in my eyes. I told him how grateful I was for everything he'd done for me. He'd helped me adjust to a new place. He'd been a major factor in the Torah growth I'd experienced. And he'd gotten me my *shidduch.* Yet the moment was heavy because I knew that he and my other friends wouldn't be at my *simchah*.

Danny went with me to the airport. On the way, I told him how worried I was about the wedding not being a happy occasion because my friends wouldn't be there. Danny told me not to worry. He was confident it would be a very happy wedding, and he'd daven for me that I'd be a joyous *chassan*.

The day of the wedding arrived. I walked into the hall and stopped short.

My ten closest friends from the Mir stood there waiting for me. Behind them, I saw three full tables of my childhood friends.

It was all thanks to Danny. He'd made all the arrangements. He'd gotten funding to subsidize fifty percent of the cost of the tickets from a donor we'd frequently been to for Shabbos. Danny had arranged for my father and father-in-law to cover another 25 percent, and the rest my friends paid for themselves.

Danny also arranged for a luxury bus to drive from my parents' neighborhood to the wedding hall, plus he'd notified, encouraged, and convinced my friends and acquaintances to come to my wedding. He was in Yerushalayim, but he had connections throughout America.

I had no words to express even part of the gratitude I felt toward him. He'd pulled off a major production, bringing in people, resources and funding, organizing and transporting everything—and all to bring joy to a *chassan*: me.

Nine years passed. My wife, Dassy, and I lived near my in-laws. I was privileged to remain in *kollel*, to continue growing in Torah. We were blessed with two boys and a girl, *bli ayin hara*.

Nine years, and Danny was still single. Even in a yeshivah the size of the Mir, you don't find too many thirty-four-year-olds still single. Danny still had the same *koach* and *bren* in learning as he'd had when I first met him, and he was still a big *masmid*. My wife and I davened nonstop for Daniel ben Rivkah to find his *zivug*.

And then it happened. *Baruch Hashem*, in the middle of Chanukah, as we neared our ten-year mark, we got the news that Danny was engaged. Our happiness doubled when we learned that his *kallah* lived in our area and that after their marriage Danny and his wife planned to live not far from us.

The *chassan* and *kallah* notified everyone that they'd waited long enough and wanted the wedding to be as soon as possible. They set the date for Rosh Chodesh Adar, adding another measure of joy to that already joyous month.

Though it was crystal clear that no matter where that wedding took place, we'd be there, the hall they booked was in Ohio of all places, right where we live, only an hour's drive from our home.

Rosh Chodesh Adar. Danny's wedding day had arrived. And this is where our story really begins.

On the way to *kollel*, my mind was on our daughter, who wasn't feeling well. My wife and I hadn't gotten a chance to talk about the wedding. But so what? Did we have to talk about it every minute?

I didn't have a car, so I knew we'd have to take a bus to the wedding, which meant it would take us longer to get there. Taking the extra travel time into account, we'd planned for me to leave *kollel* earlier than usual.

When I walked into the house that afternoon, my wife was almost ready to leave.

"Wow! Good thing you came home early today of all days," she said to me with a knowing smile. "Did you pick up on something? It doesn't matter. I arranged for a babysitter. Let's go."

I didn't know exactly what I was supposed to pick up on, but okay. The main thing is she was ready. The truth is, I thought we'd be taking the children with us to the wedding, but my wife is more of an expert on kids.

Outside, a taxi was waiting. My wife opened the door and announced with a flourish, "Happy early anniversary."

Uh-oh. What was going on?

"Where exactly are we going?" I asked her.

"It's a surprise! Wait and see."

I didn't say a word.

After an hour and a half's drive in the opposite direction of the hall, the driver pulled into a small park, and there, on a set table, awaited a wooden sign with the day's schedule and plenty more: to the left of the list was a map with small stars indicating the destinations we were to visit according to the plan. I looked at the map and realized the route planned would take us further and further away from where the wedding hall was located.

Dassy was standing there, glowing with delight at pulling off this big surprise. She told me how she'd planned it.

"If I'd waited for the actual anniversary date," she said, "you wouldn't have been surprised, so I moved it up by three days!"

There was more.

"Wait till you see all the fun things we're going to do! And," she said with a flourish, "I've arranged a babysitter until tomorrow afternoon!"

My heart sank.

It dawned on me that, one, she didn't remember that Danny's

wedding was that night, and two, she'd been planning this for quite some time. She'd booked a room, ordered tickets. I didn't know what to do.

I told her I needed to make a phone call because it all came as a real surprise and I hadn't notified the evening *kollel* that I wouldn't be coming. My wife looked pleased as punch at seeing how she'd really surprised me.

I walked a short distance away and called one of the *gedolei roshei hayeshivos* here in the States. I said I had to speak with the Rav. They told me the Rav was in the middle of receiving the public and couldn't speak with me. Regretfully, I veered from my policy of only speaking the truth and said that it was a matter of *pikuach nefesh*—which wasn't true. But I knew that if I said anything else, I wouldn't get to talk to him, and there'd be a question of *"mipnei darkei shalom."*

Within two minutes, the Rav was on the line. I told him everything, and the instructions I was given were crystal clear: continue on with my wife's entire plan and forget about the wedding.

The taxi drove us down the road to a big lake, where we rented a boat. Then we went paragliding. And finally, the cherry on top. My wife had called the wedding hall where we were married. She'd heard that the hall was free that night, and she'd asked to rent out the *yichud* room for dinner, to return nostalgically ten years back.

We arrived at the hall late at night. My wife told the taxi driver he was free to go. We'd ended our travels for the day.

The area was desolate. The hall is located below the main highway at the end of a winding descent. In the valley in which the hall is located, not a single soul was to be seen at that time of night. In the hall, there were only two staff members, busy setting up for a bris the following morning. My wife told me that the *yichud* room was ours for two hours that night. After that, the workers had to finish their tasks, leave, and lock up. Then we'd climb on foot to the main highway to the motel where she'd booked us a room.

∢   ∢   ∢

It was two-thirty in the morning. The staff had left. It was very quiet. There was hardly any noise from the highway above us. At this time of night, traffic is sparse, almost nonexistent.

It was just the two of us, my wife and I, standing at the event hall's locked gate, sharing memories of ten years earlier. It was long past the time when we should have climbed up to the road above. But as I stood there next to the gate, I wasn't ready to leave. I tried to describe to my wife the feelings that the gate evoked in me.

I told her how worried I'd been that our wedding would be stiff and lifeless. How I would hardly know anyone there. And then, I described how I felt when I stood there at the entrance and saw my friends from Israel and dozens of my childhood friends. Tears spilled down my cheeks. My wife was certain those tears were tears of emotion at remembering the amazing wedding we'd had. She couldn't know that they were tears of pain for a different wedding that had probably ended an hour earlier—the wedding of my best friend. It had probably been a quiet, dull affair because of the age of the *chassan*, whose friends, even if they had come, would be missing the spirit and gaiety of youth. I thought about the *chassan*, who probably didn't understand where his best friend had disappeared to when only a decade earlier, he'd done his utmost to give him a fantastic wedding.

My tears took me far down memory lane, and my wife enjoyed my emotional reaction.

Suddenly, we heard a deafening boom. Then the sound of

glass shattering and the smell of burning metal. A moment later, there was silence.

We knew it could only mean a car crash. A car must have veered off the highway above us and tumbled down the embankment.

We ran to where we thought the noise came from. Halfway down the slope, we saw an overturned car with fluids pouring out of it. Gas, oil, water, and blood. Any minute it might roll further down the hill or explode.

Dassy called 911.

I climbed up to the car and pulled open the passenger-side door with strength I didn't know I had. I saw a woman dressed in a bridal gown sitting inside and next to her, someone who looked very familiar.

It was Danny. Daniel ben Rivkah.

With amazing *siyatta diShmaya*, both were fully conscious. The car was still hanging over the abyss. My wife and I managed to extract them gently, first her and then him, and move them away from the car.

Her condition didn't seem serious, but Danny looked severely injured. An ambulance soon arrived, and Danny was placed on a stretcher. The bride in her white gown stained with blood and soot climbed into the ambulance after him.

Just before Danny lost consciousness, I heard him murmur, "I knew there was no way we wouldn't meet at the wedding."

A minute later, the car rolled into the abyss and burst into flames.

Less than two weeks later, Danny and his wife were released from the hospital.

We were told that the original plan was for the *chassan* and *kallah* to spend the wedding night somewhere close to the hall, but the *kallah* preferred to go straight to their new home. Danny agreed. While driving, Danny was overcome by the accumulated fatigue of wedding preparations and the wedding itself and lost control of the car.

I'd wanted to repay Danny for everything he'd done for me by attending his wedding, but Hashem had His own plans. He knew just where to place me on Danny's wedding night—in the exact spot where Danny and his new wife needed us most.

That's my story. Nothing made sense, but then everything made sense. It's not just the personal story of my wife, Dassy, and I, or the story of Danny and his wife. It's a story of revealed Divine Providence, a peek at Heavenly accounts, which we will never understand or know.

To those who are curious as to how my wife made such a mistake (and what a mistake!) about the date of the wedding, the answer is, as she told me later, she remembered the wedding was on Rosh Chodesh Adar, but she thought that meant *aleph* Adar, so she prepared the surprise for *lamed* Shevat, which was actually the first day of Rosh Chodesh.

Another thing. In the end, I hadn't broken my "resolution" to only speak the truth. The *shailah* I asked the Rav turned out to be truly one of *pikuach nefesh*—in a way I could never have imagined.

Begin Again Now

They say that after a year, you can already tell how the marriage will turn out.

They say that after seven years, all uncertainties are gone...for better or worse.

What are the chances that after twenty years of an unhappy marriage, something will change?

This is a story that will bring hope even to those who've given up.

This is a story that deals with one of the most important things in life: marital harmony.

My role here is that of close friend and confidant. Before sharing this story with you, I sought and received the agreement of all parties involved. They think it's an important story to tell, as long as their privacy is guaranteed.

He came from a traditional family that lived far from the

main population centers. After elementary school, unlike his friends who continued on to high school, he insisted on attending yeshivah.

Due to the gap between the level of early education he'd received and that of most boys entering yeshivah, he had a hard time adjusting. And at the end of the year, the *rosh yeshivah* told him, "You're not a good fit for this place. Find another yeshivah that's more on your level."

He was a quiet guy. He didn't know quite what to do with this. He didn't even tell his parents. The summer break found him dejected and worried.

Elul arrived. His mother packed his suitcase, and he went "off to yeshivah," knowing he had no yeshivah to go to.

Instead of going to yeshivah, he traveled to Bnei Brak to Rav Chaim Kanievsky. Thirty years ago, it was still easy to get in. Rav Chaim stroked his cheek and said, "I don't know you, but I know you're a good *bachur.*"

"So what should I do?"

"Go to the *rosh yeshivah* and tell him I said not to make trouble."

The *bachur* went to the *rosh yeshivah.*

"What are you doing here?"

"Rav Chaim Kanievsky told me to ask you to take me back."

"Is that what he said?"

"No, he said something else."

"What?"

"That I should tell you not to make trouble."

He was sure the *rosh yeshivah* would throw him out, but to his surprise, the *rosh yeshivah* laughed and said, "If that's what he said, then you're in. But I'll go talk to him."

He entered yeshivah with a burning desire to prove himself. By the end of winter *zman*, he was one of the top five boys.

At this yeshivah, there was a policy to award a prize to the best students. When the *rosh yeshivah* gave him his prize, he said, "Thank you for forcing us to let you stay."

Three years later, he entered a renowned *yeshivah gedolah.* He grew in Torah and *yirah* until it came time for him to marry.

Girls were suggested to him, and he went out with quite a few before finally meeting one who seemed right for him.

They met several times. He'd already made up his mind, but she was having a hard time deciding.

She dragged out the process, wanting another date and then another until finally, he asked her to give him a yes or no answer.

She asked for one more date, and then she agreed to marry him.

When they got engaged, the parents on both sides made no financial commitment. They were from families that did not belong to the *chareidi* sector and were unfamiliar with the practice of helping the young couple by buying them an apartment and furniture. The couple had to arrange everything on their own.

Two weeks before the wedding, she told him over the phone that she didn't feel well.

He came to visit her at her home. She was open with him and said she wasn't really sick, but she was struggling with the decision. She still wasn't sure about the *shidduch,* and she didn't really want to marry him.

He didn't know what to do with that information. "Why didn't you say so at the beginning?" he asked.

She explained that she'd always dreamed of marrying a tall, handsome, self-confident guy. "A knight in shining armor," she called it. "But I saw there aren't too many knights like that around. When I met you, I didn't like what I was seeing, but I knew you were a quality boy, so I said to myself, *He's not your knight in shining armor, and he's not that tall or handsome, but you always have a hard time making decisions, so just go ahead and do it.*

"But now I regret it," she said.

"What do you suggest?"

"I don't know. You decide."

The *bachur* went to talk with a highly esteemed *mashgiach*.

"If she wants you to break the *shidduch*, let her go ahead and break it," the *mashgiach* said. "But you don't do anything."

She didn't break off the *shidduch*. That was the other side of her inability to decide. And so they moved forward toward the wedding.

The last Shabbos before the wedding, the *bachurim* came to make him happy, but he was broken, crushed. He paced like a caged lion and kept asking himself, *How can I marry someone who doesn't want me?*

He returned to the *mashgiach*, who said, "You're right. I'll speak to her."

Just before the wedding ceremony, the *mashgiach* whispered that he'd spoken with the *kallah* and had reassured her. He said he'd convinced her she'd made the right choice, and now she no longer had any doubts about it. She was walking to the *chuppah* confidently.

Hearing that infused him with enormous strength. The wedding was perfect. He was the happiest *chassan* in the world.

And very naive.

When the couple arrived at their new home, a letter from the *kallah* awaited the *chassan*. In it, she asked him to forgive her for everything she'd put him through and sincerely promised him that she was marrying him in love, friendship, peace, and companionship.

The letter was my suggestion. As someone close to her in age and friendship—and I can't say in what way—I stood by her side throughout the dating period and also during these difficult moments.

Things went downhill fast, even during *sheva berachos*. She was filled with regret, and when there's no excitement, all differences are magnified. Suddenly, he seemed too quiet, too *frum*, too scrupulous.

Their marriage started off on the wrong foot, and living near her parents added to the discord between them.

His in-laws weren't the only ones who found fault with him. The whole family, which for some reason had known about her doubts all along, all joined forces against him. They even encouraged her to leave him.

He had to deal with alienation and disrespect from his wife's family, but what really bothered him was knowing deep within that he was living with a woman who just didn't like him. While he respected her, liked her, and did everything he could to please her, she didn't want to see it, and when she did see it, she disparaged it.

The contempt was the worst. All his attempts to please her and let her have her way made him look weak in her eyes. But when he tried to act a little tougher, as he'd been advised, she hated him twice as much for not understanding him and for being too strict in his Torah observance.

Sometimes she'd put him down in front of others. When they went to her parents for Shabbos, she ignored him. Her disdain was obvious, especially compared to the respect her sister gave her husband. She smiled at him and greeted him happily, while his own wife embarrassed him or just ignored him completely.

My husband and I felt very sorry for him. It hurt to see my best friend acting like this. Whenever I pointed it out to her, she'd take herself in hand and try. But it never lasted long, especially with the people around her giving their tacit approval.

One day, after her whole family had practically lynched him, attacking him one by one and all together, he decided to go to Rav Simcha Cohen, who told him, "Pick yourself up and move to a different city."

And that's what he did. She was against it at first. But for some reason—and this is one of the miracles in the story—she agreed to go along with the move.

The move brought about a major change. The number of fights and criticisms on her part dropped dramatically. But there was one thing she failed to do.

To like him. The husband of her youth.

Years passed. They had five children. We talked several times a week. She would say good things about him, but in the next breath add, "I just can't make peace with it. I don't really like him. I shouldn't have married him. He's not my soul mate. Poor thing, it's not his fault. He treats me well, and he doesn't do anything bad to me, but those are the facts."

While still in *kollel*, he began to work in *kiruv* and had a lot of success. Secular couples found him easy to talk to and through him were inspired to become religious. He became a rabbinical figure without anyone appointing him. It wasn't long before he started giving lectures and became a popular, sought-after speaker. More and more people returned to Judaism and began keeping Shabbos and doing mitzvos because of him.

His activities didn't have any financial backing since he wasn't part of an organization and hadn't been appointed to any position. After a while, my husband suggested that he travel abroad with a group of experienced fundraisers to get donations to support his important work.

And so they flew off. While I was sorry my husband would be gone for three weeks, she was very happy about not seeing hers. Which didn't surprise me.

The trip to America changed everything.

During their stay there, the fundraisers were taken around by a driver who was not religious, to put it mildly. He was on his phone the whole time, and his topics of conversation and the language he used were unpleasant.

While all the other fundraisers took it in stride, her husband couldn't bear it. He spoke to the driver and asked him to show some respect and not use inappropriate language. He also appealed to the driver's higher self and said such speech wasn't fitting for him.

While everyone else made the rounds of shuls and began collecting first thing in the morning, my friend's husband spent the first half of every day sitting and learning, giving up potential donations worth hundreds of dollars each day.

He would call his wife and cry that he wasn't happy there, that the place was spiritually wrong for him. She would tell me what he said, and I'd say to her, "Now do you see what a special person your husband is?" I'd tell her what my husband said about him. He was very impressed with him and told me in these words: "He doesn't belong here. He's a great man, immersed in Torah, truly G-d-fearing. He's far above others. He shouldn't be here."

One day, a conference of very wealthy people took place. The fundraisers took the opportunity to go there and collect. After only five minutes, her husband went back to the car and said, "I don't go to places like this. People aren't dressed modestly. There's nothing for me there."

The driver said to him, "Are you sick or something? This is the crème de la crème! You can make two thousand dollars here. Go back in there like everyone else."

"If this is the top, I prefer the bottom. It's not worth any money I might make if I have to mingle with people like that."

They returned home. He brought back half of what the others got, but he had no complaints. In fact, it was my husband who complained. "Is that how Torah is rewarded? I've been traveling abroad to fundraise for years, and I have never seen a collector sacrifice to such an extent for his principles. Why should he be the one to come back with less than the rest of us?" My husband said the other fundraisers felt the same way.

I told this to his wife. "You have a very special husband," I said to her. She was silent. I didn't know what her silence meant. Was she joining in the admiration? Or was she mad that he'd gone and ruined things?

But two weeks later, she called me, all excited.

"You won't believe what I'm going to tell you," she said. "We got two letters from the States. It seems that people noticed how my husband acted when he was there. They see plenty of collectors, they wrote, but he was truly outstanding.

"They said that people in the shul saw him sitting and learning there every morning while all the others were making the rounds. And the story of his refusal to remain at that conference due to lower standards of modesty made waves.

"What did you think they did?" she asked me. I could hear the excitement in her voice. "They raised money for him! They sent him a check for five thousand dollars, more than any of the other collectors brought back."

But the second letter he got was even more surprising. It was from the driver. He wrote that he'd been driving fundraisers around for twenty years and had become very cynical about the whole subject (I won't go into what he said).

"At first," he wrote to the husband, "when you criticized me, I got mad. But when I saw that you were giving up money for your principles, it made me realize that you walked your talk. My job is to work on rich people to get them to give their money to others. I'm not against the rich or for the fundraisers. I only care about the percentages I get. I never thought I'd get caught giving money to a fundraiser." Enclosed was a check for three thousand dollars.

As she read me those two letters, I detected, for the first time, a note of pride in her voice.

That same week she attended a seminar for her husband's *baalei teshuvah*. Afterward, the women came up to her one after the other to tell her how special her husband was. Two of them even told her they were jealous. Suddenly her perception of her husband shifted.

When she called me later, she said, "I feel completely different about him."

She said little more than that.

That was eight years ago, and it was a turning point in their marriage. From a couple with big *shalom bayis* problems and a wife who didn't appreciate her husband, they became *the* couple. From a wife who looked down on her husband, she became a wife who looked up to him with real admiration. From a woman who kept saying, "I can't feel anything for him," there now suddenly flowered between them the "love, friendship, peace, and companionship" she'd promised.

The woman's family did an about-face too, maybe because they saw she was happy and that was good enough for them. They gave him the respect he deserved. They took pride in his accomplishments and looked up to him.

I can't go into more detail, but this story can give hope to all couples who've spent years suffering with *shalom bayis* issues. Some have given up. This absolutely true story is big news. The situation can turn around even after twenty years.

Emotions can't always be explained, and we can't know what will connect husband and wife. For this couple, the husband's persistence, the respect he had for his wife, and the fact that he "followed her in the wilderness, in a land not sown" eventually proved themselves in the end, and the Creator of the world graced them with *shalom bayis* and unshakable love.

Shabbos Leave

An irreligious soldier eagerly waits for war to break out.

Sounds strange? Turns out, it's a common enough wish among combat troops.

Yet who can foresee what awaits him and his friends?

A moment before, destiny intervenes and turns the tables.

I was born in northern Israel, where I grew up in an irreligious home. Aside from Kiddush on Shabbat, I knew very little about Judaism except a few general concepts absorbed by virtue of living in the country. My parents' goal was for me to become a career officer. I attended a four-year military academy and went straight from there into the army.

Ever since I was a kid, I'd wanted to become part of an elite combat unit. I dreamed of being a heroic figure, adored by his troops as he led them into battle. It didn't remain just a childhood dream, either. I worked hard to make it happen. I excelled in my studies at the military academy, and I did my compulsory army duty as a fighter in the elite Egoz unit.

Now that I'm familiar with the *chareidi* world, I can point to one similarity between *chareidim* and *chilonim,* and that's—*lehavdil elef alfei havdalot*—the desire to be accepted into a top yeshivah. While the two things are as different from one another as east is from west, still, they share one thing in common, and that's the desire to excel and be the best.

From a teenager's point of view, why would anyone want to go to a yeshivah that makes so many demands of him? Why would he want to commit to so many hours of study and to such strict adherence to set times for learning? Why would he agree to abide by all sorts of rules and regulations when he could enter a yeshivah for the faint of heart and do whatever he feels like?

With all the disadvantages and pitfalls of the teenage years, there is one noticeable advantage: the strong desire to star, to achieve, to be a winner.

I know. It's a weak comparison. And it's wrong. But if my saying this gives even one boy the inspiration to try to get into the best, most demanding yeshivah, that will be my reward.

Now, back to my story.

By the time I'd completed eighteen months of basic training followed by advanced commando training that pushed us to our limits, I'd turned into a sophisticated war machine.

Only one thing was missing.

War.

If you've never been there, you won't understand. But at that age, after a year and a half of service, when you're filled with adrenaline and less so with foresight, you're just itching to see combat. You live, breathe, eat, and sleep army. You learn to be a fighter, you constantly push your limits to the max, and all that's missing is to prove yourself in real life, in the field.

"Luckily" for me, I was going to get my chance. Tensions flared on the northern border, and we were brought to the base located next to Moshav Beit Hillel. From there, you can get in your car and drive a few minutes, and you're already at the border. There, my comrades and I set up ambushes along the northern border.

We waited impatiently for face-to-face combat against Hezbollah, but time dragged on with no sign of war on the horizon.

Eight months went by, eight months of routine operational procedures with nothing to break the monotony. The area was quiet. Only later did we find out why. Hezbollah quiets things down to lull the enemy into complacency.

Meanwhile, instead of fighting, we spent time swimming in the Hasbani River, waiting impatiently for the order to go out on a mission. We drilled thousands of times, occasionally going home on leave. And here's where I ran into a conflict I think is common to many secular youths.

On the one hand, I was on top of the world. You have no idea how a soldier in the Egoz unit feels as he walks among ordinary mortals. On the train, in the streets, in his community, people worship the ground he walks on. He's at the top of the pyramid. He's got the world in the palm of his hand. And when I say "the world," I'm talking about the pleasures of the world, nothing meaningful or essential.

It's a huge conflict. You're primed for life, but there's nowhere to go. It's like stepping on the gas of the most powerful car with the gear in neutral. You're going nowhere. It's built into the system. After you've enjoyed yourself, the pleasure fades, and nothing's left but an empty feeling, and you wonder why you even exist.

Our unit had quite a few *kippah*-wearers, and somehow they convinced me to put on tefillin every day. One day, one of them, Rafael Muskal, told me, "Yair, I see you're becoming religious, and there's no entertainment here on the base anyway, so why not try to keep one Shabbat with us?"

I wasn't sure about that. I don't know why. Putting on tefillin and saying a few prayers was one thing. But a whole Shabbat?

"I don't know," I said to Rafael. "Keeping Shabbat seems a little too *gadol* (big) for me."

"I agree," Rafael said. "This Shabbat is Shabbat HaGadol."

"You're kidding, right?" I tell him. I had no idea what Shabbat HaGadol means. I thought he was taking advantage of my ignorance to invent a new holiday. One time, they did that to me. They told me there was a fast on *yud lamed* Shevat. I fell for it hook, line, and sinker, though no such date even exists. Later they told me they just wanted to dump guard duty on me. We all laughed, but it left me suspicious of religious holidays I'd never heard of. I wasn't going to be taken for a ride again.

"So," I said to him skeptically, "what's this Shabbat HaGadol?"

He opened a book and proved to me that the Shabbat before Pesach is called "Shabbat HaGadol."

As long as he wasn't out to make a fool of me, I was game. That was the first Shabbat I ever kept.

You know what? I enjoyed that Shabbat. It was the first time in my life I'd felt real satisfaction. Even after it ended, the sweetness of it stayed with me. Everything I'd felt, the *kedushah*, the *zemirot*, the *tefillot*. The peacefulness. It all stayed with me, and I found myself waiting for the next Shabbat.

In fact, after that first Shabbat, I had a hard time carrying out operations on Shabbat because they involve Shabbat desecration. I found it hard even though it was explained to me that it was allowed due to *pikuach nefesh* and so on. I became *frummer* than the *frum*.

Then came the news that two soldiers, Ehud Goldwasser, *Hy"d*, and Eldad Regev, *Hy"d*, had been kidnapped near the Lebanese border.

As fighters in Egoz, we knew we'd be the first to go in after them. For months, from dawn till dusk, we'd prepared for just such a situation: marches, running, shooting, firearms operations, simulation of action with real artillery masking, helicopter rescue exercises. What's interesting is that the spot where the kidnapping took place is the exact spot where we'd practiced. As if anyone could foresee the future.

But we didn't pile into a helicopter and chase after the terrorists like we'd practiced. Instead, we took up positions while the air force did the job.

You've probably read about "air force shelling," but reading about it is one thing and experiencing it is another. It was one of the most massive aerial attacks ever. The shelling went on without letup. Between two and three thousand bombs were dropped on Lebanon, and I'm talking about bombs that turn cities into craters.

So there we were, grumbling about how the air force was taking over the job and not even leaving us any crumbs.

I can't find anything in my life that I wanted more than to go into Lebanon and put into practice everything I'd learned that past year and a half. I wanted to face armed terrorists, hand grenades, and shells. Maybe this sounds wacky to you, but that's how I felt, and so did all my buddies.

And then, one night, at 2:00 a.m., there we were, faces

blackened, in full camouflage, lying under a bush on the northern border. A friend was lying right next to me, and he seemed a little unhappy about something.

"What's wrong?" I asked him.

"I'll tell you what's wrong," he said. "They're sending me tomorrow to some base in the center of the country to show new recruits what a model soldier is supposed to look like. Why now, just when we're getting our first taste of action? How can I leave you guys now and not go into Lebanon with you? I can't even think of it."

Boy, did I understand him. We'd been primed for months to eliminate those terrorists, and now when we finally had the chance for real battle, he had to jog with recruits. The poor guy.

I didn't say anything. His disappointment hung in the air. Suddenly, a thought popped into my mind. *Why don't I do him a favor and switch places?*

I didn't dare say it. Why should I switch places with him? I wanted to fight as much as he did. Why should I make such a sacrifice for him?

No sooner had I asked myself the question than the answer came to me. Shabbat. I'd been thinking that I might want to learn more Torah and try to keep Shabbat a little bit better. I said to myself, *So you'll combine doing a favor for a friend with keeping Shabbat.* Besides, who knew if we'd see any action in Lebanon? So far, they'd kept the ground forces out of the picture, and it didn't look to me like they'd be changing that policy anytime soon. The bombings would continue, there'd be an agreement, and that would be it. Back to normal. Who dreamed of us seeing action?

"I'm willing to go instead of you," I said to him.

"What? Why?" he wanted to know. "Why would you do that for me?"

"I'm becoming religious, and it's almost Shabbat. I don't think we're going in, so I'm not going to be missing anything."

"Wow! That's great. Thanks."

By three in the morning, we were already back at the base, wiping off the black face paint. The commander came up to me and said, "Yair, you have fifteen minutes to decide. If you really want to replace him, tomorrow morning, you go down to the divisional training base to start training to become a recruitment sergeant welcoming the next batch of fighters into Egoz."

The truth is, I always wanted to be a commander in the army. And now, it was my chance to be a sergeant in command of three squad commanders and to be our officer's right-hand man.

My eyes were blinded from Above. I was sure there would be no ground campaign in Lebanon. If I'd known for sure we were going in, I never would have left and missed what we'd spent eight months waiting for.

The next morning found me near Binyamina, the base for new recruits.

Who could have known that my desire to keep Shabbat would save my life?

First, a few words of clarification.

I was a point man, which means the soldier who leads the troops into battle, guiding them through unfamiliar territory using maps, GPS, and other tools. This is the most exposed position in a combat formation. To my left stood a machine gunner. Between us is the commander with the liaison behind him, followed by everyone else.

My fighting method was to always be two steps ahead of everyone else. I had to be the first to know what was happening in the field. I would scout out the area—footprints, mud, electrical wires, signs, animal tracks. I was totally in the moment. They would always shout at me that it was dangerous because if shooting started, I could get shot by friendly fire. They wanted me to stay in line with them. But it was something I couldn't control. No matter what, I'd always be a few steps ahead of everyone.

Two days after I left for the brigade's training base, it happened: the IDF entered Lebanon.

The first ones to enter the village of Maroun al-Ras were the Egoz forces, led by my company, nicknamed the Benji Force.

Heading the unit was Major Benjamin (Benji) Hillman. On his left was the permanent machine gunner, Rafael Muskal, who had gotten me to keep that first Shabbat. To his right, replacing me was Gal Rosenthal, the one I'd traded places with. Unlike me, he walked behind Rafael Muskal, not in front of him. After them came liaison Liran Saadiah from Kiryat Shemoneh.

At 9:00 a.m., they advanced in broad daylight (a very dangerous move), knowing they were entering a village filled with Hezbollah terrorists and not a single civilian. The terrorists would all be armed to the teeth like a regular army, not like Palestinians with a knife or rifle.

They were attacked by a volley of Sagger anti-tank missiles. The point man of the company was killed instantly. Rafael Muskal took a direct hit. Major Benjamin (Benji) Hillman and liaison Liran Saadiah were also killed. Gal Rosenthal, who'd stayed instead of me, was seriously injured. Had I been there, I would have definitely been killed because I was supposed to be in front of Muskal. I would have taken a direct hit from the missile.

As soon as I heard on the news that Egoz was hit, I drove like the wind to Ziv Hospital in Tzefat, where the wounded had been airlifted by helicopter. When I got there, I was informed of what I'd already realized myself: I'd been granted the gift of life.

Everyone knew I should have died. Given the way I operated as point man, I would have been hit first.

Three days later, we went through the terrible tragedy of multiple funerals.

On Friday, at the funeral of Rafael Muskal, I eulogized him. From there, totally broken, I went to my first Shabbat in my new yeshivah, Yeshivat Tikun HaMidot, headed by a tzaddik named Rabbi Yosef Shubeli.

A couple of months later, I returned to my unit to fight. All that time, the fighting in Lebanon had continued, but the minute I returned to the base, I was told, "Yair, today they closed entry to Lebanon to the infantry. Yesterday was the last entrance."

It's like they plucked me out before two months of danger and returned me exactly when it ended.

Today I live in Tzefat. I'm married and the father of six children, *baruch Hashem*. I established a Chassidic *chareidi* family, *baruch Hu u'varuch Shemo*. I tell stories with music in the background but focus on stories of tzaddikim that everyone can benefit from hearing.

I chose to tell you my story, with a special emphasis on Rafael Muskal, *Hy"d*, my comrade in arms and the man who introduced me to Shabbat HaGadol. I can still picture him, and I know his impact on my life will never be forgotten. May this story be an aliyah for his *neshamah* as well as for that of my other army buddies: Benjamin "Benji" Hillman, *Hy"d*, and Liron Saadiah, *Hy"d*.

Sorry Times Two

A childless couple embarks on a journey of forgiveness...and discovers that at times, you don't even know you've hurt someone.

And it doesn't even occur to you to say you're sorry.

Then it takes a special miracle to reveal to you from whom you need to ask forgiveness.

My story took place almost twenty years ago, but I think it's relevant today as well.

We were married for ten years, and we still didn't have children.

I'm going to skip over all the suffering and hardship we went through, both because the situation has already been described in several of your stories, and also because this story isn't about the difficulties, but about how they came to an end.

In the ninth year, after going to all the doctors and all the rabbis, we decided to go back to Rav Chaim Kanievsky, who had told us right at the beginning, "You will have children." He just hadn't said when. We'd received blessings from him, but this time we wanted to know what we should take upon ourselves to help us merit having children.

Somehow we managed to get in to see him at a time when no other people were there. I told him what we were going through. Rav Chaim again said, "If Hashem wills it, you will have children." Then I asked, "Please… Is there anything specific we can do to remove the obstacle that's causing the delay?"

The Rav thought a little and said, "*Slichos.*"

I said to him, "*Kevod Harav*, of course we say *Slichos.*"

"Ask for forgiveness from the person whose feelings you've hurt."

Now I understood. The Rav felt we should ask forgiveness from someone we'd hurt.

Outside, my wife and I started to think of whom we might have hurt.

I must say that we're pretty soft-spoken people, and we hadn't hurt anyone we could think of. I was very surprised that Rav Kanievsky said we should apologize.

We brainstormed together but couldn't remember anyone we'd hurt.

Then my wife said, "Maybe there's someone we didn't actually hurt but who felt hurt by us."

A few minutes later, we had it: the Cohens (not their real name).

This was a couple whose *shiduch* we'd made, which is a story of its own. They were frequent guests of ours. What do I mean by "frequent"? They'd sit there without moving for days on end.

A few years earlier, we'd invited them for Succos. After Havdalah, they decided to extend their stay to include Friday and Shabbos.

On *motzaei Shabbos*, my sister and her husband and two children came to visit. The next day, my parents came as well.

Our two-bedroom apartment now hosted four couples plus children. We could no longer accommodate the Cohens.

We were certain they'd understand the situation on their own and head for home. But guess what? They didn't understand the situation, despite my parents and sister "discussing" aloud who would sleep where. Somehow, the Cohens didn't think the discussion had any connection to them.

It was a very unpleasant situation. Night fell, and they were still sitting there in the living room, the same living room where my sister and her family were supposed to sleep. My parents had already gone into the room where the guests had slept previously and settled in there.

There was silence.

At one point, my sister couldn't help but ask, "Um, who are you invited to tonight?"

"We're here," Mrs. Cohen said.

"Where will you sleep?"

"Where we've slept until now."

"But my parents are sleeping there now," my sister explained.

"Then in here."

"But we're sleeping here."

"Who says?"

"They invited us before the holiday," my sister said.

"Us too," Mrs. Cohen replied.

"Yes, but I understand you've been here for three days."

"And we decided to stay on another couple of days," she said.

"So what do you suggest we do?" my sister asked.

"Let our hosts decide," she replied, looking at us.

A thick silence hung over the room. Then I said, "My sister is here from out of town, and you live only a few blocks away. Maybe for the two days she's here, you could stay in your own home."

"You're kicking us out?"

"*Chas v'shalom*," I said. "I'm just making a suggestion."

"No problem. I understand your 'suggestion' perfectly well." Turning to her husband, she said, "Let's go. There's nothing more for us here."

My wife offered for us to go to their house while they took our room. But that was it; the woman was "offended."

They left the house in a huff.

That had happened three years earlier, and we hadn't been in touch with them since.

"We'll ask them to forgive us," my wife said. "We weren't trying to hurt their feelings, but they felt hurt."

The very next day, my wife contacted the Cohens. We went to their home and asked for their forgiveness. They forgave us immediately, without any trouble, and even said that we might have been right because we'd had no other choice.

End of story.

We went away to a hotel that Shabbos.

Shabbos night, I joined the hotel's minyan. As I walked into the shul, I saw a pair of eyes glaring at me with open hostility.

I tried to ignore it, but the man kept on looking at me with real enmity. Eventually, he came over to me and asked me my name.

I told him.

"If so, I can't daven with you."

He said this loud enough for everyone to hear.

"Why not? What did I do to you?"

"What did you do to me? You really don't know what you did to me?"

"No. I don't even know who you are."

"You caused me a lot of anguish and cost me a lot of money. I'll never forgive you, and I'm certainly not going to daven in the same minyan with you."

He went around gathering his own minyan, making sure each person he asked knew exactly why he was doing so. People responded with raised eyebrows and murmurs of "Really?"

I walked over to one of the men and said, "What's he accusing me of?"

"He said you falsely accused him of hitting someone with his car, and you even testified against him in court."

Suddenly it clicked.

I knew just who the man was.

The incident had taken place several years previously. I had been sitting in my car when I noticed a policeman writing a ticket for a luxury car. The office was standing behind the vehicle. Suddenly, I saw him fall, and the car drive off.

I was shocked. I got out of the car and went over to the policeman to help him.

He stood up by himself and asked me, "Did you see what happened?"

"Yes."

"Give me your ID. If anything develops, you can testify that he hit me."

I gave him my contact information, and a few months later, I received a court summons to testify about what I'd seen.

I hadn't seen the driver because the car had tinted windows, and I never knew the outcome of the court case.

Only in the hotel did I hear from others that the driver was slapped with a big fine and had his license suspended for six months. He also had to do community service, which to him, was worse than all the rest.

"Let me ask you a question," I said to them. "What would you have done?"

Some said, "You're right. You did just what you should have."

Others said, "I wouldn't have gotten involved."

"If it had been your son who was run over, would you still say it's okay for someone who was there not to get involved?"

They had nothing to say to that, but I could see they weren't on my side.

"I don't think this is a coincidence," my wife said after I told her what happened. "Maybe this is what Rav Kanievsky was talking about when he said to ask forgiveness. You might not have meant to hurt him, but he felt hurt. Go ask him to forgive you."

I approached the man, but he didn't even want to talk to me.

All that Shabbos I sent people over to him to explain my side of it. I asked them to tell him I hadn't even known who was in the car, and I'd only gone over to the policeman to help him, and I hadn't meant to hurt anyone.

All he would say was, "The bottom line is that you made a lot of trouble for me, and I'm not ready to forgive you for it."

By *motzaei Shabbos*, he seemed to have softened some-what, because he davened in the same minyan as I did. But he was far from being ready to forgive.

My wife and I were very upset. Beyond the shame and

distress we experienced at the hotel, we knew we needed this man to forgive me so that we'd merit children. But we didn't see any way to make him agree to forgive.

What happened two days later was nothing short of a miracle.

I went down to city hall to take care of some personal matters. Two people were in the elevator when I stepped into it. Suddenly one of them said, "Here's the fellow who helped me get back at a guy who mouthed off to me."

I recognized him as the policeman who'd fallen.

Something about his tone alerted me that I should try to find out more about what had happened.

I smiled and winked at him so he'd feel I was on his side. I waited for the elevator to stop and followed him out. A minute later, I approached him like a fellow conspirator and said, "So what happened in the end?"

"The judged slapped him with a heavy fine. He barely escaped a prison term."

"But what did he say to you that made you do that scene with the fall?"

"You know those people who have a million-shekel car and feel like they own the world? When I went over to him, he said to me, 'You can write anything you want. Just make sure you don't get my windshield dirty with your papers.' You hear the chutzpah? I said to myself, *I'm gonna teach this guy a lesson.* I stepped back and pretended to fall. I went to the healthcare center, they gave me two days sick leave, and you put the final puzzle piece into place."

"Ha, ha, ha," I laughed, but inside I was thinking, *If he can put on a good act, so can I.*

"Listen," I said to him, "you've chosen the wrong profession. You should be an actor, not a policeman."

He chuckled and said, "Don't worry. I combine both. He's not my first, and he won't be the last."

We parted affably.

When he was out of sight, I took my cell phone from my shirt pocket to see if the record function I'd surreptitiously activated was working.

It was. Perfectly.

From there, I went to the office of the man I'd testified against.

I came without an invitation. I just walked into his office and said to him, "I messed things up, but now I'm going to fix it."

I sat down next to him and played him the recording from start to finish.

He couldn't believe his ears. "Where did you get this?"

"Should I start at the beginning?"

"Of course," he said.

I told him about our family situation, that we had no children, about Rav Chaim Kanievsky telling us that we should ask for forgiveness but we couldn't figure out from whom, and how that very same week HaKadosh Baruch Hu brought us in contact with a person we hadn't known we'd hurt as well as the policeman who gave us the opportunity to fix things.

He became very emotional, and his eyes filled with tears. He stood up, hugged me, and said, "I forgive you with all my heart. Now I'm fully convinced that you acted in all innocence and with absolutely no evil intentions. People tried telling me so on Shabbos, but I was still too angry to hear it. Now I understand that I must have needed to go through whatever suffering was involved in order to atone for my sins. I forgive you completely.

"*Machul lechah, machul lechah, machul lechah,*" he said.

"And give me your name and your wife's so I can daven for you to be blessed with children."

I sent him the recording, and we agreed that through his lawyer, he would contact the police and get the court to dismiss the charge.

I went straight home, elated. I sat down with my wife and told her about the incredible miracle Hashem had sent my way. We both felt it was too big for us to comprehend. What were the chances that in the same week Rav Chaim Kanievsky told us to ask forgiveness I'd "happen" to be at a hotel far from my hometown and meet up with the man I'd harmed, and that two days later I'd "happen" to meet the only person in the world who could reveal to me that the man I'd testified against was really innocent? And more, that Hashem would also give me the ability to set the record straight.

The recording did its job. It took time, but in the end, the dishonest policeman was arrested and confessed. A retrial took place, and the owner of the car was acquitted of all charges. He was reimbursed for the fine, and he even received compensation for the public service work he was forced to perform through no fault of his own.

But the amazing ending of the story happened even before that.

A month after the meeting, against all odds, my wife found out she was expecting—exactly as Rav Chaim Kanievsky had told us many years before. And nine months later, she gave birth to our son, who is now nineteen years old.

The bris was held at the Lederman shul, and the couple we'd hosted and to whom we'd apologized attended. The distinguished businessman also made sure to be there. Our shared story formed a bond between us, and he felt part of the miracle that happened to us. He gave us a substantial gift, which proved he had truly forgiven me.

Our firstborn was followed by six more children, and every so often, someone will say, "You must tell people your story."

We chose to tell it to you and your readers all over the world, and I hope its message will resonate with them: You need to apologize to everyone you've hurt—even if you don't think you hurt them...and even if you really didn't.

My Father's Seder Plate

All I wanted to do was give my parents a fancy Seder plate as a gift. But my father surprised me by giving me in exchange a rusty tin Seder plate you'd be ashamed to be seen throwing out.

Before I could decide whether or not to take offense, he told me the story behind it.

After so many years of presenting other people's stories in People Speak, I hope you don't mind letting the author tell his own story about himself and his beloved father.

We spent Seder night with everyone at my parents' home in Haifa. And when I say everyone, I mean *everyone*: married children and their spouses plus the grandchildren.

I'd thought about what would make a good gift for my parents and immediately decided on a replacement for their Seder plate.

Their Seder plate is... Well, let's just say it doesn't resemble any Seder plate you've ever seen or could imagine. It's a round, dented, over-sixty-year-old piece of tin that might once have been silver-plated but then again, maybe not. What is certain is that it's lost all its silver and is left with only rust stains.

We kids always laughed at this Seder plate. We said it would be better to use the plastic Seder plates we brought home from *gan*. Naturally, we didn't share our opinion with our parents, maybe because we were afraid they'd take us up on the offer.

Anyway, I found myself buying my parents the biggest Seder plate I'd ever seen. You know, one of those enormous pieces of sterling silver with three tiers and two doors for the matzos, crowned by a huge silver plate with indentations for all the symbolic foods.

As you can imagine, I felt pretty pleased with myself as I placed the new Seder plate on the set table and said, "Abba, finally, at the age of eighty-three, the time has come for you to have an elegant Seder plate, as you so rightly deserve."

My father got very upset. To someone like him who grew up in Batei Ungarin, a Seder plate like the one I'd brought was an outrage and totally unacceptable. Had I given it to him in previous years, chances are he would have thrown me out to live inside in the monstrous Seder plate I'd bought him. But for some reason, my father had softened, and instead said to me, "Chaimleizer (Chaim Eliezer), I accept this gift on condition that you accept an even costlier gift from me."

I was curious to know what costlier gift my father was going to give me in exchange for this impressive Seder plate, but before my imagination went wild (and it knows very well how to go wild), what did my father do if not pull out the dented tin plate that has served as his Seder plate for as far back as I can remember. And what he does he say in the tone of an oligarch who's just bestowed upon his son his three hundred-foot yacht with seven decks and two helicopters, an outdoor and indoor pool, a barbershop and a restaurant, which cost him about $175 million, if not, "Chaimleizer, it's yours."

I didn't know whether to laugh or cry. The whole reason I'd bought the Seder plate was to get rid of the dented, rusted piece of metal our family was stuck with. And, frankly, I had wondered if I should ask a Rav if the halachah of *genizah* (or any other halachah for that matter) applied to it. And here my father was gifting me with the old Seder plate, guaranteeing it a place in the family for a few more generations. How was I going to get out of this one?

"Abba," I said to him sorrowfully, "I think this Seder plate has served its purpose. It's, how shall I put it, no longer useful. It lost its silver years ago, and it doesn't exactly add sparkle to the Seder table."

"If you knew the story behind this Seder plate, you wouldn't talk like that," he said.

A few hours later, at the Seder table, during *Shulchan Orech*, he told us the story.

My father, may he live and be well, was three years old when he arrived in Eretz Yisrael with his family on the *Skaria*, an illegal immigrant ship.

The Walder family took its first steps in Eretz Yisrael in Batei Ungarin, without relatives or friends. It was only the husband, wife, and four children.

My grandfather, Moshe Alter Walder, was a well-known *baal tefillah*. He earned a living working at the Friedman metal manufacturing company. Savta Golda Leah was the one who kept the home fires burning, to the extent that when the Jordanians shelled Meah Shearim, and their home was almost completely destroyed and the family was relocated to a spacious home in the Katamon neighborhood, immediately after the bombing ended, she moved the whole family back to Meah Shearim, to the bombed-out, half-destroyed house. Thus, she guarded her family from any foreign winds that might harm their pure education.

Meanwhile, more children were born. They had no income, which wasn't uncommon in Yerushalayim back then. At the age of sixteen, my father was sent to learn in the Chachmei Lublin Yeshivah in Bnei Brak under Rav Shmuel Wosner, *ztz"l*, where he became his *talmid muvhak*.

My father received two lirot from his parents on which to live. He lived in poverty and want, but didn't complain because he didn't really know any other life.

As if that wasn't enough, after marrying off a daughter, my father's parents sank even deeper into poverty. There wasn't even enough money to buy a table, so the family made do with a makeshift table and mismatched chairs.

To give you some idea of the poverty prevailing back then, the yeshivah went to Meron ("Not on Lag BaOmer," my father emphasizes. "In Elul."), and my father was really starving. He walked to a nearby moshav where, just like today, there was a kosher restaurant.

"Is there anything to eat for fifteen *grush*?" he asked.

The restaurant owner explained to him that the cheapest food started at forty *grush*, and my father turned to leave. Then he heard the man's wife say to him in Hungarian, "Maybe we can push the fish heads on him."

Fish heads were considered a real delicacy in the Walder family (and still are, by the way). The man asked my father if he wanted some fish heads. My father put on his most woebegone expression and said, "I have no choice" and got a meal fit for a king.

Which reminds me that when my father arrived at Chachmei Lublin Yeshivah, his friends noticed a strange behavior. My father used to check the fish for worms. His friends asked him for the source of his practice, and he answered that he didn't know, but his parents always did it, so he did what they did. He got a few raised eyebrows and even a few snide remarks, but as you've probably noticed, my father is not one to be impressed by such things. They could do what they wanted, and my father would continue to maintain his family *minhag*.

One day, out of the blue, *Hamodia* newspaper printed an article about worms being found in fish and how important it was to check fish carefully before eating.

At the Wagshal hall, possibly the only event hall in Bnei Brak back then, panic ensued. They had no problem with the necessity of checking the fish they served, but how exactly was it done?

One of the yeshivah students overheard the discussion and said, "I don't know what you need, but we have some weird Yerushalmi in our yeshivah who checks the fish." My father was quickly summoned to the Wagshal hall, where he was given the permanent job of checking all the fish. His pay was two and a half lirot per wedding. Remember, this was a *bachur* who didn't have more than fifteen *grush* for a meal.

As if that wasn't enough, the Holigman shul desperately needed a *baal korei* to replace the Yerushalmi they'd had who'd just gotten married. Even at that young age, my father was asked to be the *baal korei*.

"It was a nightmare," my father told me. "It was a demanding shul headed by Rabbi Meir Karelitz, *ztz"l*. They would correct you for every little mistake. You'd even hear shouts from the *ezras nashim.* But all the humiliation was worth it," said my father. "I got five lirot for reading on Shabbos, and there were two minyans, so I could earn forty lirot every month just from the Torah reading. And that's in addition to my fish business, that is, checking for worms at Wagshal."

Thus the *bachur* Shlomo Walder saved up lira after lira, tens after tens, and hundreds after hundreds. And like a proper Yerushalmi, he didn't waste a penny of it.

Do you think he was stingy?

Not at all. Because after two years of saving up the money he earned by hard work checking fish and being a *baal korei* at Holigman, on Purim of 1956, my father bought a new table with six matching chairs and had them delivered to his parents' house.

Along with the table and chairs so badly needed, he added an item to be used for the upcoming Pesach Seder.

"And that is the Seder plate I am giving to you now as a present instead of the tower you gave me," my father said to me. "After my father and mother died, my siblings decided, and rightfully so, that I was entitled to it. Now I'm passing it on to you for the coming generations."

Then he showed me the engraving on the plate, which I'd never noticed before because I'd never bothered to take a close look at it. It said: "This Purim *shalach manos* gift is presented to you by your beloved son Shlomo. Purim 5716 / 1956."

At that moment, I realized the Seder plate I'd bought wasn't worth even the slivers that fell from the engraving on that priceless bowl from sixty-three years ago. I hadn't gotten just a Seder plate as a gift from my father, may he live and be well, but a shining example of the love and devotion of a young boy to his father and mother, and a true illustration of the commandment "honor your father and your mother."

Dutifully chastened, I took that Seder plate and guarded it more closely than any *afikomen* I'd ever found. And when I returned home after the holiday, I put it in the silver display case for all to see, turning down a friend's suggestion that I have it restored and replated.

Aside from its emotional and educational significance, and it being a statement of *"v'higadeta l'vincha*—and you shall tell your son," it seems to me the most beautiful and eye-catching item of all the many silver objects in my home.

Glossary

The following glossary provides a partial explanation of some of the Hebrew and Yiddish, (Y.), words and phrases used in this book. The spellings and explanations reflect the way the specific word is used herein. There may be alternate spellings and meanings for the words.

a"h: acronym for *"aleha hashalom,"* peace unto her, added to the name of a deceased woman.
achi: lit., "my brother"; said to a fellow Jew to express closeness.
amecha Yisrael: Your people.
avreich (pl. *avreichim*): a young married Torah student.

b'siyatta diShmaya: with the help of Heaven.
baal teshuvah (pl. *baalei teshuvah*): a formerly nonobservant Jew who has returned to Jewish tradition and practice. Also, anyone who repents of behavior not sanctioned by the Torah.
baal korei: one who reads the weekly Torah portion aloud at prayer services.
baal tefillah: one who leads the prayer service.

bachur (pl. *bachurim*): a young man; a yeshivah student.

baruch Hu u'varuch Shemo: blessed be He and blessed be His Name.

bashert: one's predestined mate.

bein adam lechaveiro: the mitzvos between man and his fellow.

bein hazmanim: semester break in the yeshivah schedule.

beis medrash: the study hall of a yeshivah.

ben sorer u'moreh: a stubborn and rebellious son.

ben Torah (pl. *bnei Torah*): lit., "sons of Torah"; those who learn Torah.

bimah: the reader's desk in the synagogue on which the Torah scroll is opened and read.

bitachon: trust in God.

bli ayin hara: lit., "may there be no evil eye," an expression meant to ward off possible misfortune.

Borei Olam: the Creator.

bren: (Y.) lit., burn; fiery enthusiasm while learning Torah.

chalilah: God forbid.

chamin: cholent.

chareidi: an ultra-Orthodox Jew.

chas veshalom: Heaven forbid!

chassan: a bridegroom.

chassidishe bachur: a young Torah student from a Chassidic family.

chaval: "What a shame!"

chavrusos: study partners.

cheder yichud: the room a bride and groom enter alone as the final stage of the wedding ceremony.

chillul Hashem: desecration of God's Name.

chilonim: Jews who haven't yet begun keeping the Torah.

chinuch: Jewish education and upbringing.

chol hamoed: the intermediate days of a festival

chuppah: a wedding canopy; a wedding ceremony.

chutznikim: boys whose homes are outside Eretz Yisrael.

chutzpah: insolence.

daas Torah: the Torah perspective as stated by an outstanding Torah sage.

dati: religious.

dayan: judge in a religious court.

derech: lit., "path" (off the derech: off the path, i.e., no longer religious).

dvar Torah (pl. divrei Torah): short speech expressing Torah thoughts.

emunah: faith in God.

emunat tzaddikim: belief that Torah sages can be relied on to give the correct advice based on their deep understanding of the Torah.

ezras nashim: the section of a shul synagogue reserved for women to pray.

frum: (Y.) Torah observant; pious.

frummer: more pious than average.

gadol: a leading Torah authority of the generation.

gadol hador: the leading Torah authority of the generation.

gan: kindergarten.

gedolei roshei hayeshivos: the heads of the leading yeshivos.

HaKadosh Baruch Hu: the Holy One blessed be He.

Hashem Yisbarach: the blessed One.

hashgachah: Divine Providence.

hishtadlut: effort.

Hy"d: acronym for Hashem yikom damo, "May Hashem avenge his blood"; used when speaking about a Jewish martyr.

kallah: a bride.

kedushah: holiness, sanctity.

kehillah: community.

Kevod Harav: lit., "Honored Rabbi"; a respectful form of address used when speaking to a distinguished Torah leader.

kibbud av: showing proper respect to one's father.

kibbudim: lit, "honors"; distinguished roles to perform at the wedding ceremony.

kiddush Hashem: sanctification of God's Name.

kippah: a yarmulke.

kiruv: bringing nonreligious Jews back to their heritage.

Kisei HaKavod: G-d's Throne.

kittel: a long white garment worn at the Seder.

Klal Yisrael: the Jewish people.

koach: energy.

kollel yungerman: a young married man who learns in a yeshivah for married men.

kollel: a center for advanced Torah study for adult students, mostly married men.

l'chaim tovim u'leshalom: lit., "To a good life and to peace."

l'chaim: to life.

lehavdil: said to distinguish between sacred and mundane.

lehavdil elef alfei havdalot: the differences are so great there is no way to compare them.

ma'arav: west.

machloket: disagreement.

mashgiach: a spiritual guide in a yeshivah.

masmid: a diligent yeshivah student.

mechilah: forgiveness.

mechutan (pl. *mechutanim*): (Y.) the name given to the relationship between the father of the groom and the father of the bride.

mesader kiddushin: one who conducts the marriage ceremony.

middos: character traits.

mizmor: a psalm that is sung.

motzaei Shabbos: the night following Shabbos, after the sun sets.

Glossary

nachas: pride; satisfaction; pleasure.

neshamah: (lit.) "soul."

netz: sunrise, the earliest time of day to pray.

nisayon: a Divine test or challenge.

pasken: (Y.) to issue a halachic ruling; colloquially, "to judge."

pikuach nefesh: a matter of life or death.

ratzon: A time of Divine favor when prayers are especially likely to be answered.

sefer (pl. *sefarim*): sacred book.

segulah (pl. *segulot*): a supra-logical action that has practical effects.

seudah: a festive meal in celebration of the day.

seudat Shabbat: a festive meal in celebration of Shabbat.

shadchan: a matchmaker.

shalom aleichem: lit., "Peace be upon you"; a hearty welcome.

shalom bayis: lit., "peace [in the] home"; marital harmony.

Shechinah: the Divine Presence.

sheva berachos: the seven blessings recited at a wedding and also at any of the festive meals held in honor of the bride and groom during the week following the wedding.

shailah: lit., "question"; a question posed to a Torah scholar about how the Torah wants one to act.

shidduch (pl. *shidduchim*): a marital match; dating for the purpose of marriage.

shlita: an acronym for "may he live long."

Shulchan Orech: The part of the Pesach Seder when the meal is eaten.

simchah (pl. *simchas*): a joyous celebration.

siyatta diShmaya: Heavenly assistance.

talmid muvhak: prized student.

talmidei chachamim: Torah scholars.

tefillot: prayers.

tovel: immersion in a mikvah for the purpose of purification.
tzaddik (pl. tzaddikim): extraordinarily righteous person.
tznius: modesty

vasikin: (Y.) earliest minyan that prays at sunrise.

yerei Shamayim: lit., "one who fears Heaven"; a sincerely religious
   person.
yerachem Hashem: lit., "[May] God have mercy."
yeshivah bachur: a yeshivah student.
yeshivah gedolah: a yeshivah for post-high-school-age boys.
yeshuah: salvation.
yichud room: see *cheder yichud*.
yirah: fear of Heaven; piety.
yiras Shamayim: fear of Heaven.
ym"sh: *yimach shemam*, may their names be blotted out.

zecher tzaddik livrachah: may the memory of a righteous person be
   a blessing.
zechuyos: merits.
zemirot: songs sung at the Shabbat meals.
zivug: predestined spouse.
zman: lit., "time"; one of the three semesters in a yeshivah year.
ztvk"l: acronym for *zecher tzaddik vekadosh livrachah*, may the
   memory of a righteous and holy person be a blessing.
ztz"l: see *zecher tzaddik livrachah*.